VILLAGE PEOPLE

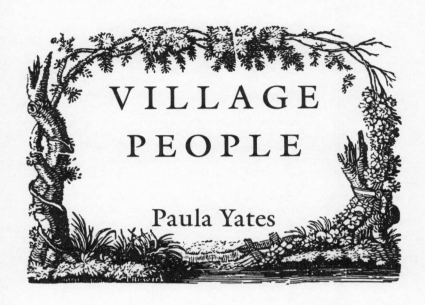

VILLAGE PEOPLE

Paula Yates

LITTLE, BROWN AND COMPANY

A *Little, Brown* Book

First published in Great Britain in 1993 by
Little, Brown and Company

Copyright © Paula Yates 1993

The moral right of the author has been asserted.

*All characters in this book are entirely fictitious
except, of course, Daniel Day-Lewis. The situations
in this book are imaginary, and bear no relation
to any real event or person, except when they're
about my friend Sue!*

Illustrations on pages 17, 27, 29, 46, 63, 79, 81, 93, 124, 140, 151, 153,
189, 199 by Rex Whistler, taken from *Down the Garden Path* and
A Thatched Roof by Beverley Nichols (Jonathan Cape).

A CIP catalogue record for this book is
available from the British Library.

ISBN 0 316 90589 5

Typeset by Solidus (Bristol) Limited
Printed and bound in Great Britain by
BPCC Hazell Books Ltd,
Member of BPCC Ltd.

Little, Brown and Company (UK) Limited
165 Great Dover Street
London SE1 4YA

This book is
dedicated to Miss Read
for all the hours of bliss
I have spent reading her books.

But also to Sue, my muse,
the most beautiful, exotic bloom
in any garden in Kent,
with all my love as always.

AUTHOR'S NOTE

Since I have lived in the countryside, I have been enthralled by the passing of the seasons, and the different events which punctuate the calendar of any small town in England.

It is these seasons and delightful events which have inspired this book and, although the characters are fictitious, I have tried hard to accurately record the joys of country living.

Paula Yates

CONTENTS

AUTUMN

WINTER

Ten Years Ago

I ADJUSTED THE SHINY RED HELMET AGAIN, almost garrotting myself in the process. Then I shifted from one numb buttock to the other, before attempting the pelvic floor exercises I'd read about in *Woman's Realm* to alleviate my tension and regain some feeling in my rear end. For well over an hour I had been gripping our motorcycle seat, a thin strip of hard brown naugahyde, clinging on to it with ferocious intensity as we drove rather wildly through the horrors of South London and out towards Kent.

As we came off the motorway, on to what finally looked like perfect English country lanes, a wasp flew into my open visor, so we screeched to a halt to bat it away. The trees along this route were vast, covered with big pink candles of blossom that swished rather poetically in the breeze from the bike. Despite the wasp attack I had to leave the visor open as it was so hot that day, so the wind blew furiously into the opening, filling my cheeks up with air so I looked like a very surprised lurcher with its head hanging out of a station wagon.

On either side of the road there were orchards full of gnarled low trees, their branches dipping almost down to the ground, heavy with fruit. Sheep grazed in between the trees, contemplating which blade to eat next, gazing out into the middle distance and occasionally looking myopically at each other. The skies above us tumbled along, perfectly blue filled with vast puffed-up clouds that listlessly floated past. A tiny plane was directly overhead making a lazy trail of white across heaven.

My husband stopped the bike by the side of the road. I thought that he'd got another gnat up his nose, but he just took off his helmet, swept a long sweaty tendril of hair out of his face and wiped a bit of spit off his chin rather Byronically, which isn't easy. Slowly taking off his sunglasses, he seductively looked up at those vast blue Kentish skies. A bird trilled, a bee hummed blissfully from one honeysuckle flower to another.

'Wow,' he said peering intently like the sheep into middle distance. My heart thrilled. He is so at one with nature I thought ecstatically. 'Wow,' he repeated slowly, wiping his nose pensively with the back of his gauntlet, 'That cloud over there looks exactly like Elvis...'

By now we both longed to get off the bike, but we were also determined to view a house that we knew was up for sale. Ten years ago when all of this happened I was six months' pregnant with our first child Harmony and we wanted to leave London fast, although perhaps not quite as fast as we were now travelling.

Sitting on the back of the bike I was an unfortunate cross between Orca the Killer Whale and one of those red bratwurst you can eat at bierkellers in Munich. I was definitely not the right shape for spending the morning on the back of anyone's throbbing engine. Girls who do that with aplomb, especially on hot days, always have long flat blonde hair, so that when they take their helmets off it won't have mutated into what appears to be two Shredded Wheats with a sweaty centre parting. They always wear black leather catsuits with studded gussets, and are accompanied by louche-looking boyfriends sporting dazed armadillos down the fronts of their jeans. In no *Easy Rider* movie does the heroine hop off the bike clad in a floral marquee with a white pique Peter Pan collar and size 16 American Tan support tights with a built-in 'breathing' knicker. Like me that faraway summers day.

So there we were, speeding along the little winding road ruffled on either side like a flamenco dress with vast drifts of cow parsley. It's a little known fact that cow parsley was originally introduced to Kew Gardens as a giant curiosity plant stretching up to eight feet tall, and from those few plants, seeds escaped over the wall summer after summer, eventually populating the entire countryside with those tiny ethereal flowers hanging off huge empty stalks, and filling the air with that unimaginably delicious smell, which is an almost bittersweet fragrance like a flower crossed with a trainertamer. Even now, when I am in the woods at the end of our garden in late summer and they are filled with slightly wilting cow parsley, the smell is so evocative that I am transported back to that luminous hot day, which was so still and quiet the only sound was the roar of our engine and the sizzle of the tiny pools of tar on the road beneath us.

The hedgerows on either side of us were proper ones as still exist in Kent, dotted with clumps of wan-looking dog roses with their washed-out complexions. At one point a little river trickled along, drifting slowly, filled with darting minnows and long strands of snotty green slime. By now I longed to throw myself sideways off the stinking bike, unceremoniously pulling off the clinging support tights and putting my feet in the limpid cool depths. Instead I simply scanned the bank for water voles and contemplated my bottom which was now feeling nothing. I vowed to myself that when I was a country dweller I would have a pony and trap like in a Beatrix Potter book, and wander about wearing a flattened old straw hat to shade me from the glare of perfect English days. Never again would I have to travel at more than four miles an hour with my legs wrapped around a red hot exhaust pipe.

People who move to the country tend to fall into three distinct categories. Members of the first group move into enviably exquisite thatched cottages but still decorate them in exactly the same way as the penthouse pads they had in Docklands where they had a rave party every Wednesday for fifteen friends from an advertising agency. They never get to know their country neighbours, have a matt black rubber floor fitted throughout, and possess two lone Bauhaus tubular steel armchairs and an avocado on a glass coffee table as their sole concession to clutter.

The second group is made up of people who think they have to look like farmers, but get it all wrong because everything is so horribly new. They buy it all at Simpson's, and everyone knows that farmers pass clothes down from generation to generation. When new people arrive in the country, they immediately rush out and buy all the 'essentials'—brand new Range Rovers with a silver model of the Monarch of the Glen clamped on the front, ghastly pukey green anoraky things with ghastly matching tartan-lined wellingtons, ugly chicken-shaped casserole dishes, stable doors for the kitchen like in *Mr Ed the Talking Horse*, and invariably a big Aga with three hops stapled above it, continuously dropping leaves into the mulled wine.

Naturally, being a rather fragrantly old-fashioned person I come into the third and—luckily for Kent—rarest category, otherwise it would be run like an Amish community with no electricity or fax machines. This includes the newcomers who have read one too many Miss Read books about the countryside and want the whole thing to be preserved in aspic. They have to lie in a darkened room if anyone mentions the Channel Tunnel, never want to see anything modern again, and dream of having a parlour maid who occasionally fights with the tweeny.

These people invariably sport clothes they obviously bought from a Merchant-Ivory production, droopy cotton frocks printed with old roses with uneven hems.

They spend their days surrounded by a herd of children who all look like Ukrainian refugees, wandering their gardens, occasionally snipping with a pair of shiny secateurs at the drooping blooms of a massive cabbage rose or filling a trug with dead heads. Trug! The mere word conjures it all up. Say it loud and you see a garden, say it soft and it sounds just like a moorhen being sick.

With our family about to expand we had decided on the English countryside as the perfect spot for our bonding—I yearned to retreat as much as possible from modern life. I wanted to recreate a make-believe world glimpsed in books, where men in cravats bound in and out of the french windows inviting anyone for a tennis party, or those BBC period dramas set in the halcyon days between the wars when men were called Bletherington-Smallpiece, tea was served on the lawn under an awning and a pot noodle was something made in a kiln.

Ten years ago that rural dream was what I wanted, and I vowed that day as we sped towards our destination that no packets of Birds Eye frozen kedgeree would ever darken our Shangri-la ...

There were a number of reasons that we wanted out of London. To fill our lungs with the potent aroma of sheep dip mingling headily with the eye-watering smell of fertilisers being sprayed on to the yonder fields ... In truth, the main reason was that bricks and dustbins were being thrown through our front window in London with alarming regularity as various youths launched themselves into the living room and made off with the video.

Our local burglars had no intentions of emulating

PROLOGUE

Raffles, that much was clear. Not for them silver, pictures, family heirlooms or even the kelim-covered club fender. Instead it was straight for the telly, the toaster and, worryingly, on the last three visits attempts had been made to roll up the large orange twisty shag fun fur on the bathroom floor. In fact we had even developed a personality profile of the burglar—a colour-blind man who liked watching old films on TV while eating toast, and probably had a house with several lava lamps and cheetah print bri-nylon sheets on his water bed.

On his last call my husband arrived home unexpectedly and caught him filling a small cardboard suitcase he'd thoughtfully brought with him with various gold discs, obviously thinking they were solid gold. Husband, thrilled to the core having seen far too many episodes of *The Professionals*, made off in chase, leaping nimbly over walls topped with broken glass, risking all future generations of our children before rugby-tackling the burglar, who, having been traditionally garbed in a striped tee shirt with a woolly balaclava on back to front, had found his progress across the South Circular Road somewhat impaired.

The burglar stabbed him resolutely and efficiently straight through the hand. The victim lay there tenaciously holding on to one leg, as the gold discs spilled all over the road, and the local policeman ran towards them across the Common. Then three little boys came over to ask for the wounded soldier's autograph ...

For me I think the deciding factor in moving was that I wanted more space for our dog Growler, a small

Yorkshire terrier in desperate need of thorough colonic irrigation. The smell of fertilisers held no fears for me after a year of living with Growler, a dog genetically incapable of being house trained. In the end we'd even sent him to an obedience school where he spent two weeks living like an extra on *Tenko* before emerging with a special commendation because he'd learnt his name.

The final straw came one morning as the rain drizzled down and the wind blew in through the hole in the window where a bicycle pump had been flung in the night before. As grey light from the street bounced off my cellulite, turning me to the colour of a dead trout, I slipped the entire length of the hall on a terrible attack of Growler's diarrhoea which he'd succumbed to the night before having consumed from our ripped-open bin bag two chicken biryanis and a Vapona fly-strip. Once you've experienced that barefoot, you realise it's time for the dog to spend more time outdoors.

Compton Pauncefoot is somewhere between Whitstable and Canterbury and is well known for its quaintly preserved antiquity. It is Disneyesque in its Little England way, with each house delicately painted white and picked out in pastels. It is the sort of small town where a browning begonia in your hanging basket can actually result in a public stoning at the Saturday market.

The town is in a valley, well protected from the bad

weather most of the time, but luckily always prone to a white Christmas to keep local painters happy. The town, its allotments and all of the surrounding countryside is quite dedicated to producing fruit, vegetables and flowers, all of which are bigger, better and more technicoloured than those elsewhere, not that I want to boast too much about the size of our leeks.

The town centre dates back to mediaeval times, and has a rather beautiful Tudor market place; the local brewery is a perfect example of Victoriana picked out with pale green hops in massive relief all over its walls. On festive days, such as the Annual Torchlit Procession when local beauty queens sit in all their polyester glory on the back of Ford Transits being pelted with boiled sweets by onlookers, the whole town takes on a truly Breughel quality, filled with higgledy-piggledy little houses tumbling over one another, and fat, red-faced housewives with meaty arms leaning out of their upstairs windows watching the passersby.

So, if in my dreams I yearned for Old Englande, nostalgic for what it should have been but probably never was, then we found it that afternoon, preserved in amber, lit by firelight and always ready to be eccentric at every opportunity.

'There's the house, up there,' my husband bellowed over his shoulder like Bullwinkle as we sped towards a steep hill. I was close to boiling point and my face stung like a big, round, smacked bottom. Despite having started the journey as a veritable cauldron of new life, I now felt like a used condom flung in a canal.

But I was already charmed by the magic of Compton

Pauncefoot. To our left was the duck pond, surrounded by trees in blossom and weeping willows trailing pale green fronds in the murky depths, where eels darted and ducks flung themselves upside down intermittently to keep cool. Looming up on the far side of the pond was the old building which once held the gunpowder factory, and next door to that was a tiny row of ancient wooden cottages with gardens of astonishing colours. The urban fashion for monochrome gardens, subtly displaying thousands of plants all in the same shade of off-white, had not hit Compton Pauncefoot.

Next to the road were the allotments. Rising up from the water on the side of the hill and overlooked by the vicarage they were a cornucopia, with little brick paths winding through them all neatly bordered with pansies and asters in alternate red, white and blue. A few of the brave locals willing to risk heat stroke were stripped to the waist and feeding bottles of beer to giant marrows the size of small pigs; one sat looking wistfully at an onion the same size as a small bungalow in Southport. Occasional small wisps of pale blue smoke rose into the air and then hung there timelessly. Another gardener had unwisely misjudged the heat of the afternoon and had lit a small bonfire, heating everyone up even more and annoying anyone planning to have a good dig that afternoon.

The road was now rising steeply. Squinting, I could see a huge walled garden, and through the trees a tower and a house rose up, topped with a prancing golden weather vane which glinted in the sun.

'There, that's it,' he repeated. 'That churchy-looking

place is our house.' It was already our house, halfway up the hill, with a numb backside on a hot afternoon and before we'd even been inside.

We already knew some of the history of the house from its owner, whom we met when he sold us three tapestry cushions and a big tassel from his antique shop. The house was very old and had been a priory until the dissolution of the monasteries, and throughout the hundreds of years of its existence various bits had been added to it. Other bits had also fallen off, or been blown down. Part of the cloisters had vanished at the turn of the century when the gunpowder factory down the hill was blown up by a spark off a horse's hoof, littering the entire site with amputated arms and legs—after that horses had to wear little white cotton socks to prevent sparks.

Inside the cloisters, the priory had a potière garden neatly mazed in box hedges still standing in perfectly clipped splendour enclosing vast quantities of psychedelically coloured blooms obviously planted by someone on a violent acid trip. The vegetable garden was the oldest part of the property. It had once been a Roman burial ground, and the rest of the garden was filled with summerhouses and tiny follies built by various owners since the nuns moved out.

By the time the present owner moved in the priory was a private house, and he too had added his own modernisations, including a power shower so strong that it was capable of acting as a water cannon, giving a shock to anyone within a three-mile radius if they were standing in the wrong position when it was switched on. This shower, it was rumoured locally, was single-handedly responsible for the hosepipe ban in Kent.

And so the bike chugged up the hill, our baby kicked lazily around inside me and I longed for a dandelion and burdock ... As we turned into the drive, we passed a little gatehouse. Its carved gables depicted local birds and a variety of small furry creatures and a couple of gargoyles on the top of the drain pipe had been added for macabre effect. And then it was as if we were in the depths of the countryside, not in the middle of a small Kentish town, for atop the hill you could see no other neighbours through the surrounding trees, [although we later discovered it was possible to stand up on the brow of the hill overlooking the allotments and the pond to admire the heat-hazed view below, stretching out towards the municipal baths and the cricket grounds].

The paddock which was directly in front of the house was surrounded by a ha-ha to keep the flock of sheep inside safely. And also for future children to topple into each summer holiday. A set of stairs to nowhere stood next to the front door for those needing assistance in mounting their horses, although at that stage of my pregnancy I could have done with them to get into my tights. A typical English country house herbaceous border stretched along the side of the paddock with hollyhocks, delphiniums and lilies of every shade jostling for a good position.

The huge, heavy door creaked open revealing an empty *Ivanhoe* set within. It looked almost completely dark after the glare outside, though slowly our eyes adjusted to the lilac light within, streaming in through the stained-glass windows lining the cloisters. Every single window was a myriad of tiny chips of coloured glass, occasionally punctuated with a Victorian message in heavy Gothic script telling one to not 'read a book rashly'. The foundation at the end of the cloister was surrounded by jasmine, its tentacles growing unchecked up the walls, over a window, across the ceiling and over a small seat made of bent twigs and sea shells.

From along the passageway, as it headed towards the vast door which led directly into the church itself, I could hear the distant trickle of water from an indoor fountain. They were obviously ignoring the hosepipe ban that day at least. How wonderful it would be to live next door to a church, the descants wafting through the kitchen every Sunday with the tinkle of the collection plate and the smell of incense.

'I want to live here,' I whispered intently over the drip of water.

'So do I,' came the reply from somewhere nearby in the purple haze.

A few moments later we had our first meeting with the man who has shared our lives for the past ten years. Lowther, the gardener, lives in a mock-Tudor cottage near the thatched circular summerhouse by the side of the paddock. For three decades he has tended to the temperamental pipes, the operatic neighbours and the ebb and flow of vicars next door. He also looks after the sheep, the flowers and the vegetables through each passing season, seemingly oblivious to even the coldest weather and unaware of the vagaries of any fashions.

Lowther is tall, slim and has the driest sense of humour in the country. That day and every day since he was clad for his work in greenish brown twill trousers held up with a small length of twine—which is also useful for tying up the climbing roses, and trussing up recalcitrant scouts on his days as the town scout master. He is the old-style country gent who thinks nothing of rising at dawn to do battle with vast acres of nettles which always appear to have grown overnight.

'Ar,' said he when he saw us.

He took us on the first of our grand tours of the house, pointing out carved graffiti from 1620 in the panelling, a stained-glass window depicting a violent stoning in a bedroom, and pertinent messages done in painstaking calligraphy all over the house by nuns. He explained to us that the house had once been owned by the man who did all of the stained glass for Pugin's cathedrals and he kept all the tests for the windows here. Our future bedroom had 'GOD'S INTENT NONE SHALL PREVENT' appropriately emblazoned across the widest window, and a drunken restoration scene in another.

In the drawing room he ran his gnarled nettled hands lovingly over a massively heavy tableau above the fireplace depicting the Field of the Cloth of God. 'Ar,' he said. 'Him in the red stockings standing next to the flanks of the King's white horse, he owned this house then, had this done as a souvenir of his big day.'

In the study he coughed discreetly and mentioned it had been the nun's toilet in the Middle Ages because a small river had run straight through it. He thought it odd they'd decided to illuminate that particular room with the crests and coats of arms of every king and nobleman who came to stay in the house.

Each room possessed a sense of great peace and tranquillity, especially if you'd just spent the past hour and a quarter roaring up the motorway with your cheeks like air-filled mud flaps. Great shafts of light shone through rooms scattered with floating dust and the whole house was strongly perfumed with the scent of the old-fashioned climbing roses that surrounded the cloister gardens and then grew up all of the walls, tangled with wisteria and huge coloured plates of clematis. These climbers also grew unchecked into the rooms, sneaking through the windows and resting along the sills before making their way along curtain rails made of old gondola poles. They still do today. Their fragrance combined with the smell of newly mown grass which lay outside in small piles everywhere. This house may have seemed to us like heaven on earth that day, but it was hell for the hay fever sufferer.

So we stood on the brow of the hill, looking down, thinking it was a perfect place for lots of children. We had decided that we were going to come and live here, and we could hardly believe our luck in finding it.

It was almost dusk when we finally decided we had to set off again for London, praying no one had climbed in and nabbed the shag rug. The light was slowly beginning to fade, the sheep looked a little dozy, gnats were floating about above us. A slight heat haze still shimmered above the road. Then we saw him, rising like Lawrence of Arabia out of the dust, the first thing I really noticed being a pair of pert tanned buttocks in a pair of leopard-printed thong bikini briefs, colloquially known as a posing pouch. He was bent over squeezing out a rag into a yellow plastic bucket of soapy water. He then straightened up and rubbed furiously at a chrome fin sticking up off his E-type Jag.

Slowly he heard the bike revving behind him and turned, a wide Hollywood-white smile across his face, a large silver crucifix lying on his tanned stomach.

He walked over.

'Good evening,' he said with a slight wave of his chamois. There was a pause as we both drank in the full splendour of his leopard print pants, the tanned and rippling torso. 'I'm going to be your new vicar—you must call me Lance.'

CHAPTER 1

Hell On Wheels

I HAVE JUST REJECTED—yet again—my husband's usual request that I actually stick gaffer tape across the children's mouths when we set off from the family rabbit hutch in London, a house of similar proportions to some of the deluxe hamster cages now available at Harrods, but with slightly nicer soft furnishings. For ten years now, we have been making weekend pilgrimages to heaven in Compton Pauncefoot as well as spending all the school holidays down there, but finally we have made the big decision to spend *all* our time in Kent. With three children and the still impossibly repulsive Growler—his system has worsened with age—we need plenty of space. Secretly I think my husband would prefer to spend lots of time in London, wandering around the art galleries,

admiring four-acre canvasses covered in limescale entitled 'Life'. He is definitely intent on adhering to the
Evelyn Waugh school of fatherhood, perhaps sending
me a telegram from Darkest Peru at some point asking,
'Have you had your child yet and what are you calling
it?'

As anyone with several children would tell you, one
of the great surprises is how different they all are, what
astonishing personalities emerge so young, and how
challenging it is not to throttle them when they are all
together. Children who are charming angels alone often
turn into monster beasts in the company of their
siblings, especially in the confined spaces of a car. Still,
I don't see the gaffer tape as an alternative—Honey is
rather adenoidal and would probably expire by the end
of our street if she could only pant noisily through her
mouth in any moments of repose. The littlest one,
Heavenly Delight, would find it hard to be breastfed
continuously with her gag in place. And my eldest
daughter, the Tahitian bohemian Harmony, simply
would not be able to behave like a typical ten-year-old—
surly, rude and a clever dick for an hour and a quarter.
I don't want to stifle any of their personalities.

The journey down to Kent is a great trauma for my
husband for two main reasons. Firstly, he would much
rather be in a red plastic Ferrari Testosterone listening
to a whingey Bob Dylan record, driving exactly like
someone on the last lap of the Italian Grand Prix. And
secondly, he still cannot understand why the roads are
open to other drivers when he is on them. The combination of the busy traffic out of London, the almost

continuous fighting in the back seat and the most heinous smells has been known to make him disassociate from his personality—like Joanne Woodward did in that film about the ninety-four faces of Eve.

Our usual route takes us from Chelsea, across the bridge, through Vauxhall, past the Oval, then through endless winding streets trying to avoid any traffic lights because it sends him berserk to stop for a red light. Then across Blackheath, where he simply shouts continuously out of the side window at other drivers, occasionally breaking off his quite astonishingly wide range of Irish invective to roll up the *A–Z* and swat at the dog, or round on me ferociously, mistaking me for the driver of the powder blue Hillman Imp who cut him up in Stockwell.

As we go round the last roundabout before the motorway he traditionally leaps rather athletically out of the car—often without opening any of the doors—and bangs on someone's bonnet before resuming his place in the driver's seat and merging with the motorway. This is usually done by overtaking an articulated lorry by driving underneath it at three hundred miles an hour, so that the G forces remove passengers' toupées, force one's cheek on to the rear view mirror and suck the pushchair out of the back window that hasn't actually opened for three years.

He slowly becomes the Missing Link, displaying a cathartic range of emotions, He-man and She-ra rolled into one hairy form, so sexy and vital he could easily be the man who worked the dodgems at the fair when you were fourteen. We all have to remain totally silent. With three children this is almost impossible unless I chloro-form all of us which seems a trifle excessive. Some might think that after ten years of these frequent migrations he would be used to the emotional rigours but every time—forty times a year in the past—he shouts that if I have any more children, 'I'll shoot my dick off,' or alternatively, if he's in a more mellow mood with other drivers, he merely threatens to have a vasectomy in his lunch hour.

Despite this I am looking forward to this momentous journey—I expect to only come back to town occasion-ally now, and this New Year will be a thrilling change for me. I'm feeling excited about turning into a cross between Joyce Grenfell and a Butlin's Redcoat, end-lessly making small editions of the Taj Mahal out of bars of carbolic with the aid of Harmony's local chums.

The children are in the back and I peer at them through the mirror hoping to catch anyone pinching. Harmony is asleep, long brown curls tumbling over one shoulder. She clutches her Game Boy in one hand, with her luscious mouth open and a little bubble on its corner, and I can see Honey next to her eyeing the bubble of spit curiously, wondering whether to pop it. Harmony occasionally shifts in her sleep; she is probably having an exciting dream where she simultaneously dives a perfect swallow dive off the highest board in front of an admiring throng, rides in the Grand Na-tional bareback and finds a way of stunning Honey, aged four, with a dart, possibly dipped in a milder form of curare.

Honey is sitting looking like Carroll Baker in *Baby*

Doll, wearing a pair of dirty pink nylons with diamanté on the ankle and a large hole on one knee. Her pale pink party dress has bits of Alpen stuck to it, and a thin slightly soiled feather boa is wrapped around her neck. Her face is carefully but inexpertly made-up with blue eye shadow, golden glitter on her cheeks and forehead and pink lipstick which at one point reaches her nose and then veers wildly towards one cheek. I notice that she's almost mascaraed her eyebrows and one earlobe. In her lap she is holding a small white red-eyed rabbit called Ferdipan who is a bit of a stunned mullet, but if you lived most of your life in a small pink plastic handbag you might be too.

Heavenly is strapped into her baby seat like Buzz Aldrin. She is appropriately dressed in a fur-trimmed snowsuit with a mouse print on it, and holds a baby doll, its bottle, a doll's sling and two dummies on a ribbon in her arms. She is very thin, slightly bald, and wants to be a homeopath or a midwife when she is older than two. She resembles a woodland sprite and lives up to her name.

Most of all she is worried because she hasn't seen my bosom for twenty minutes and she's going to go into withdrawal any minute.

The children are delightful until they get into our car. Perhaps someone should research this interesting phenomenon.

At once they begin a sophisticated form of guerrilla warfare. Chewing gum bought to encourage Trappist monk-style silence is stuck on to each other's hair with pliers and industrial-strength Chinese burns are applied frequently so that the shrieks of anguish can be heard as far away as Norfolk. All of this causes a maelstrom of emotion—which pet shrinks tell you an animal always picks up on—so at some point Growler invariably gets a runny bottom.

This at least keeps the children occupied opening and shutting the electric windows and blaming Heavenly for the smell. As the air actually begins to solidify and turn into a dull pea souper fog, it becomes impossible to breathe without the sun roof open. This sends Honey hysterical because it threatens to destroy her Jackie Onassis hairstyle, complete with stiff blonde flick-ups and her pink heart-shaped glasses. As she howls on a high frequency like a fridge freezer with a faulty plug we drive on through the marshy swampland of the intolerable stench ...

Meanwhile Heavenly, who is never naughty, thank God, sits pensively breastfeeding her plastic doll with her dungarees flapping open and an Earth Mother expression on her adorable face. Harmony indulges in rather monotonous music hall style exchanges with anyone she can pick a fight with, often calling us *idiotas* because she seems to think it's less likely to get her into trouble than saying it in English. Alternatively she turns on her poor sister who is valiantly clutching at her hair trying to stop it getting windswept, and calls her an oik, until even I wish we'd installed an ejector seat.

After half an hour of this stress the dog finally evacuates the remains of a Vapona fly-strip [he's grown fond of them] and the dregs of a shampoo bottle on to my husband's jacket which has fallen off the back of his seat on to the floor. He then breaks off from shouting, 'Get off the road you fat bastard,' to electrically open everything including the boot, causing Honey to become so anguished that an exorcism will probably be required. Husband stares murderously at me, and trots out the old chestnut about shooting his dick off if I ever have another child. Honey inserts a felt tip into her rabbit's anus and peace ensues.

As Honey and Heavenly happily spend ten minutes seeing how far the pen can go and then wiggling it around, Harmony leans through the gap in the front seats and mentions in a charmingly animated way that the dog has had an accident on the jacket, and that Honey has her foot in it.

'Daaaaaaaad,' she keeps saying, as though it actually is a fifteen-syllable word. 'She's an *idiota* isn't she?'

'I'll take the kids on the train if we ever have to come up again,' I offer weakly. He misses this kind offer as by now he's already sprinting along the road about to pound his fists madly on the bonnet of a red Robin Reliant containing two skinheads, their mother and her Chihuahua.

Of course, after all of this an est course in business assertiveness would seem like nirvana. When we arrive, we emerge from the car battered but with a certain trench spirit, especially the rabbit who hobbles off to the vegetable garden to recover. The impression of heavenly peace is increased by the total silence as Heavenly clamps back on to the front of me like a small brooch and Harmony vanishes with friends up a tree. Husband, who has almost had a coronary, has washed his jacket under the garden tap, and is now staggering off to the library with the *Spectator* spread over his face. Occasionally he raises the corner of the paper to mutter about how much he would love to have a little two-seater helicopter, and how I could take the children in future.

But by then the sitting-down is over for me. I only ever get to sit down when I'm in a moving vehicle and strapped into place; the rest of the time I run around like one of the last six people on earth in one of those 1950s science fiction films about a meteor about to hit Croydon. I'd have been the starlet in purple underwear who is running and twists her ankle just as everyone is about to reach the safety of a reinforced lean-to garden shed.

Lowther has filled the house with marvellous flowers, huge towering edifices of blooms with no visible means of support. Soon the scent is mingling with that of slightly charred cakes, incense and the bloody dog who has limped off to hide his head in shame before assaulting the bins again.

Honey is blow-drying her hair in a slightly darkened room, watching *Rear Window* avidly on the TV. So I leave her and stand with my head on my husband's chest, looking out over the garden.

'If I couldn't have a helicopter I'd have one of those James Bond cars with a fucking big magnet on the front.'

A scream shatters the peace as Harmony runs towards us. Her face is an interesting red and white tie-dyed effect from the mingling sweat and dirt.

'MMMMuuuuuuummm, you have to come now. I think the rabbit's bitten Honey's nose and the end might have come off.'

The New Year has begun...

SPRING

CHAPTER 2

Spring Fever A Go-Go!

SPRING IS THE TIME OF THE YEAR which separates the optimists from the pessimists in the country dweller's calendar. Optimistic country folk greet the dawn of a new year gazing out of leaded windows and delighting in the view of frost-covered branches set sootily against the massive white skies, the chill of possible snows and frosts always in the air. They admire the remnants of the Christmas snow-falls still clinging to the hills beyond the woods behind the cricket ground. The wind may blow hard, bending the trees and bushes, swaying the rushes around the pond and making the ducks swim around Cape Horn, but optimists will revel in it. While they watch the lonely bird circling, calling to its mate, they think of the cosy log fire downstairs, crumpets to be toasted, butter that will drip down chins [in my case, many chins].

The optimistic amongst us like the cosiness of it all, the fact that the rooms are filled with cinnamon candles and the lamps have to stay on all the time. The New Year is only just over, but I'm already waiting for signs of brighter weather and spring sunshine. The children and I wrap up warmly each morning to rush outside and look for hyacinths and crocuses. The ground crunches with really thick crystalline frosts like the sort of lipstick girls with white stilettoes always wear. Then, before Honey disintegrates from the stress of not looking like Blanche Dubois in a snowsuit, we all retreat for fortifying cups of hot chocolate, yet more buttery scones and crumpets, and hours in front of the fire reading and playing games—before it's time for me to venture out to fill up the shagging log basket yet again.

Pessimistic country folk wake up in bed frozen, thinking they are at a Himalayan base camp, with an interesting marbled effect on their hands and feet as though one of those weekend paint effect courses has practised on their nether regions during the night. They count to ten and then have to sprint like Roger Bannister out of bed, risking hypothermia on their record-breaking run to the toilet. The connecting passages of all English country houses are notoriously chilly and, first thing in the morning, when it is still pitch dark, it can be a sad moment of truth as you sit on the toilet, legs dangling in a force nine gale whistling from the North Face of the Eiger right up your nightie as you contemplate the ancient central heating system, which invariably requires a boiler larger than the

Titanic to make enough hot water for a cup of tea.

Thoroughly disgruntled, the pessimists amongst us then sally downstairs ready to kick their log basket [invariably empty when you most need a log] into the next county with a well-aimed size nine.

One of the lucky peculiarities of the valley that Compton Pauncefoot nestles in is that spring arrives early, blossoms and shoots burst forth rapidly and then we have snow, every four years like clockwork.

This year I first noticed that spring was in the air again when the dusty yellow catkins began waggling in the breeze. The blossom started to make the trees look like someone had pink-iced them in the night. Underfoot in the woods the tiny flowers were appearing—little violets, weeny little snowdrops braving the last bits of frost, yellow celandines and coltsfoot. Honey adores them so I took her for a walk. She wandered around with a basket, picking posies, wrapping ribbons around them, and then presenting them to us. Her little pink hands filled with flowers look so sweet that I know that soon things will be improving.

Around this time of the year the fashion magazines began their annual predictions. The forty-eight-inch bosom combined with the two-inch hip was the new shape! As usual I heard women would have two main choices. This year it was the Rampton look, pea green asymmetrical shorts with platform shoes, or alternatively mini hotpants made up of fabric based on Gianni Versace's left buttock.

All of this was always rather worrying for us country people who have about as much opportunity for pampering and facials as Grizzly Adams in the Yukon. This probably explains the predominance of shops in our area catering to the 'county' look. Ladies try to avoid the question of hotpants, preferring to stick firmly to big issues like whether to buy another A-line tweed skirt or a new quilted waistcoat with a peasant-patterned lining this year. My thighs were in worse condition than anyone else's because my dear spouse decided that he could single-handedly halt the recession by rationing the central heating to three minutes a day which meant the children all had to go to bed wearing three pairs of pyjamas and goose grease all over their faces in case they got frostbite. Consequently my body spent the long, dark winter under so many layers of clothing it had the alluring texture of a three-day-old school sago pudding.

Despite this I was filled with that familiar feeling of rebirth; a great feeling of optimism was upon me. And to celebrate this brave new world I contemplated moving our bed from one side of the room to the other, and also removing the two-pound dustballs that had formed underneath it. In with his twopenny worth stepped Husband, he to whom all change is abhorrent. Totally aghast, he would have preferred it if we were still sleeping on the straw pallet that stood in the room at the time of Cromwell. He would have liked us to use the same central heating system as then: two lumps of cow dung slowly rotating over a couple of candles for the entire house. He was baffled why I wanted to move the bed four feet across the room and was willing to fight the move with all the tactics of a latter-day Rommel.

To comfort myself, I cleared out the drawers of the kitchen dresser, which revealed a wealth of ephemera—notes from the milkman and the postman, messages from Lowther about how many ducks the fox had eaten in a month, and a wealth of old seed catalogues and special offers for rhododendrons with purple trumpeting flowers and shocking pink stamens which I covet each passing year...

For all my enthusiasm, getting into step with a new year can be hard work. Occasionally there are moments where the appeal of the big city is apparent. The narrow streets busy with throngs of shoppers, pushing each other around at the sales in vast bright shops with thundering heating systems and mountains of bargains ... this can seem rather appealing compared to the wild, cold, unlit spaces of a rural town or village.

In the frozen grey tundra of the English countryside it is the darkness of everything that forms people's patterns of living. The fact it is so forbidding after four o'clock in the afternoon means that lots of us go to bed very early, unlike in a big town where it is perpetually well lit and cinemas and cafés beckon with the wiggling finger of promise. In town nothing stops at night, and here everything shuts by half past five.

In Compton Pauncefoot you would be hard pressed to get a fourteen-course Indian meal, three videos and a rave party for afters with thousands of fellow devotees frenziedly dancing half naked and pointing at light bulbs but no doubt things will get more modern at some point. I noticed only the other day that our local video shop has now supplemented its stock of films called *Spit On My Grave 1, 2* and *3* with a selection of *Forsyte Saga* videos for anyone with unusual taste.

In summer our house seems splendid with all of the windows flung open on to the scented garden, the french windows permanently banging in the breeze and the children running wild, as they never could in the city now. But in winter there is a certain dim appeal for a narrow claustrophobic house like our old one in town, with lots of winding stairs and warm bedrooms where you break the window if you open the door too fast. Still, I'm glad I've admitted those odd disloyal moments that I've had while luxuriating in a huge bath filled with my usual ration of half an inch of lukewarm water.

In Compton Pauncefoot the shops do not particularly invite the recreational shopper, unless you are suddenly enchanted with the idea of a large leg of lamb, two feet of chicken wire and an enema bag. Here the window displays prove that most of the shops sell a multitude of different things; there is one shop in the High Street which has a window crammed with corsets, massive bras with zip-up cups for new mothers, half-slips in pistachio green and vast pairs of flannel passion-killers, decorated with plastic strips of parsley [the windows not the knickers]. Another shop sells baskets and incense mingled with gift books and candles, and has a small post office at the back. There are several butchers, a very forgetful fishmonger and a number of pubs, the one most frequented by the movers and shakers of the area being Earl Spencer's Slug Pellet. I once ventured in and was amazed at the decor which consisted of the interior of the old Tudor building, with a vast console of flashing lights around the bar and a swirling bright pink and red carpet. Compton Pauncefoot has no shops where a woman's credit card might wobble in anticipation as she approached; there are certainly no dress shops that might cause family rifts, but if you're looking for a nice firm shampoo and set you're in the right place.

As a result we are very susceptible to catalogue shopping around here. I spend hours browsing through the Sunday supplements, gazing longingly at extendable loft ladders and rubberised knee pads for weeding sessions. I recently sent off for a white fireproof boilersuit 'as worn by Emerson Fittipaldi in the pit' which I haven't got a great deal of wear out of so far.

I was waiting for a leaflet about log cabins, two on wrinkle creams and a coat rack that is going to 'revolutionise my life'. Sue, my best friend, who lives nearby, sent off for two sacks of narcissus bulbs and a two-pound bag of wild flower seeds—'Create a field, save the environment' she was advised. There was also a very convincing advert for a half-timbered swimming pool but I felt that on top of the row about whether we should clean under the bed that might not be wise ... Still, I admit I do sometimes yearn to hear the tip-tap of very high heels on Sloane Street and the slap of the credit card on the Hermès cash desk, and see a glittery window, rather than a bow-fronted one filled with ornamentally arranged pieces of liver.

I threw myself whole-heartedly into spring-cleaning and started with the bedrooms. Anyone would have thought that our bed was listed. It was still in its usual position and I thought I might have to give up the fight, and concentrate instead on trying to win my ongoing battle against moths which were eating anything and everything. Last year we had a massive blitz of spraying Doom into wardrobes and under all the rugs, before having to go outside and be violently sick all over the bedding plants.

I polished and pounded everything, removed thousands of spider families who had made vast impressive webs across the beams in the cloisters, and discovered a big mouse community in the little-used cupboard in the bathroom where inventively they have made bedding out of a huge package of Tampax. I also read an article which said that the reason Raquel Welch at fifty-five looked ten years younger than Bonnie Langford was that she had given up sugar and stood on her head every morning.

After our Christmas, a bacchanalian festival of face-stuffing, I had plunged myself into an abyss of self-loathing because of a definite need to wear clothes several sizes larger. Apart from admiring the Queen, opening my presents and fervently kissing Santa Claus,

I hardly ever lifted my head from the trough. I noticed that I was able to eat continuously without [a] being sick, [b] experiencing guilt, or [c] looking to the future, when my body will resemble that of a water-logged sea slug. My post-Christmas diet lasted approximately an hour. Short of having my jaws wired I still found I had to eat a lot of suet puddings to ward off wintry chills.

But Millicent always manages to cheer me up. Millicent Tring-Harcourt lives in one of the prettiest houses in the centre of the town but spends much of the year on cruises on the *QE2* where she is best known for playing her cornet on the poopdeck (she's also played the Last Post at three different funerals at sea).

The signal of Millicent approaching is usually the rhythmic slosh of her sloe gin sling in her toothbrush mug as she walks up the cloisters in her highest heels. The seventies revival began here; Millicent always wears polyester catsuits in swirling psychedelic designs with niftily matching fringed ponchos. At forty she looks thirty and has the raunchy redhead features of a sexy Rita Hayworth, if you can imagine Rita Hayworth with a gin sling in a toothbrush mug and one side of her hair slipping out of its grips.

'Happy New Year y'all hear,' she barked as she subsided into her favourite chair at our kitchen table, spilling more of her drink on the floor where Growler licked it up and then fell into a coma at her feet, occasionally emitting appalling drunken smells. 'I've come for solace,' she explained. 'I'm in agony. It's only 15 January and I don't know how much more self-denial I can take.'

The children and I gazed expectantly at her as she readjusted her catsuit gusset and swung her beads in a feisty redhead way. She sniffed loudly and turned conversationally to the baby. 'Tried to give it all up in one fell swoop,' she told her, as though Heavenly were twenty-three and attending a group therapy meeting in Manhattan. 'Smoking and drinking, but it makes you feel so ghastly I wonder if it's worth it really.'

Heavenly nodded sagely, the spectre of weaning looming before her ...

'I've felt like a bloody amputee lately, my fingers literally itching to have a ciggie in them. I gave it up as I was just sick of feeling like a disused men's club, fed up of having jaundice in two of my fingers and distressed teeth like a rabid dog's. The trouble is it's so hard to shake that feeling that you can solve most major domestic disasters with just the touch of a Swan Vesta on a fag, isn't it?

'And the drinking had to stop, I thought—well, I thought that two weeks ago. It doesn't take Hercule Poirot to realise that it was the dim memory of the Christmas office party that made me want to change my ways in that direction. Shudders can be evoked at the hazy thoughts of French kissing with the janitor on the fire escape, finishing with a tour de force performance, singing a knickerless rendition of "Will You Still Love Me Tomorrow?" from the top of a filing cabinet. It no doubt gave middle management a lot of pleasure, but several people said I was horribly flat on some notes. It was all the sort of thing that keeps a sodden culprit off the sauce till next year, although parties don't seem the same when all you've had is half a pickled gherkin and a glass of Tizer.

'I've asked myself what is life without the occasional cherry brandy? And does it really matter that everyone saw me with my sequined boob tube on in a half-nelson?' I noticed that Harmony was nodding whole-heartedly in agreement, as abstinence from any of life's pleasures is not her forte. Last year she decided to give something up for Lent, and sensibly decided on fly-fishing, which she'd never tried in her life. Despite this she felt it gave her a taste of what deprivation feels like.

Millicent and I sat there trying to work out why we both thought that, come 1 January, we were going to be transformed overnight into a mixture of Carl Lewis and the Virgin, having previously been face-stuffing - gin - swilling - nail - biting - dog - thrashing - thigh - wobbling - lazy - fag - ashing - cellulite - covered friends.

In my big effort to give up the demon sugar Millicent had suggested that I pin up a large luridly coloured photo of Cindy Crawford wearing what appeared to be a lettuce. She pointed out that there was no point in me continuing to pretend my stomach was a sarong I'd bought at the Donna Karan sale last January and it was time for ACTION. I'd be shamed into this by the sight of Cindy each morning at the crack of dawn.

But all that happened every morning was that I raced back upstairs to hop on to the scales, where I would stare down at the astonishing weight, then look around to see if one of the children or the dog had got on behind me. Then I threw myself off them again to furtively rip off two corn plasters and my earrings to see if they were making any difference to the plateau stage that I'd obviously reached after only three hours of dieting.

After four days it became apparent that all Cindy was doing was forcing me to eat vast quantities of Swiss rolls. She seemed to have an unfair advantage over me, as she was on a deserted beach miles from a Swiss roll, sniffing the ozone and attacking nothing more fattening than Richard Gere, whereas the nearest beach to us in Kent is Sea Salter where you can get gum boils from paddling too far out. It sent me into such a decline that only three bowls of porridge, a quart of thick cream and some demerara dragged me from the precipice of despair. Instead I put up a rather nice photo of Dame Sybil Thorndike. It made me feel like a sultry love goddess.

Just as Millicent was going, Lowther came in and told us that another lamb had been born. We already had six and they were adorable white fluffy things with black patches and tremulous little tails. Normally we don't expect lambs to arrive until February, and by April we can watch them playing games with each other, rushing around and hiding behind the oak tree in the middle of the paddock. For some reason this year we've been lucky and had some early arrivals.

The blackthorn around the edge of the paddock was

in full bloom, smelling deliciously but strangely of marzipan, as we made our way to welcome the new lamb, perhaps even to cuddle it if the mother was amenable.

When we first moved here I had no idea how much work was involved in keeping sheep. We wanted them mainly for their grass-eating qualities, but also for ornamental purposes. I thought they would just live out there, and occasionally keel over dead with their little legs stuck up in the air.

We soon realised that every year they have to be sheared. A local farmer kindly helps out with this, sending over his three sons to practise their skills, but over the years this has left us with hundreds of bags of wool, all of which were piling up in the garage. Finally we had it made into blankets, so it now looks like the sluice room in a wartime hospital filled with rolls of rough blankets.

Then we had to deal with the ghastly problem of their endless attacks of nits, lice and ticks, all of which were picked up and brought home by the children, cats and, of course, the damned dog. A sheep dip was erected in the field, and we had two horrendous days of chasing the sheep around without a proper sheep dog. Instead we made do with Lowther on his mowing machine followed by a hysterically over-excited Growler, propelling himself around with methane gas from his lower intestines as always.

The final cause for concern was their sex lives, not a subject any townie dwells upon at all. Our great problem was inbreeding, which led to baby lambs being born without any bottoms. The vet was always being called around to the Priory in the dead of the night to try and poke new little bums into them. This procedure is rarely successful, and if it failed certain death sadly, but shortly afterwards, would occur. Now we send some of the older sheep to live on neighbouring farms every spring when their youngsters arrive.

I still blame myself for these early tragedies, largely because of a phone call that I was convinced was a hoax from a jealous friend in London who hadn't managed to opt out into the wilds.

It happened one morning when, as often is the way, Millicent and I were sitting at the kitchen table talking about a selection of lots she had bought in a local auction, after one too many Cuba Libres at home with our friend Dorcas. She'd struggled home to discover she had acquired a huge box containing sermons written on very old paper, three Liberal peers made of pink plaster and a pole-thing attached to what appeared to be a large runner towel. It had to be plugged into a socket, then thumped, trembled and wobbled up and down while you stood to attention wrapped in the rubberised towelling bit, having your thighs pounded like a Hebridean beach. Millicent was still using it every day and even now tries to convince Dorcas to use it on her not inconsiderable charms.

In the midst of this jollity, the phone rang, and a very grand elderly lady announced herself to be Lady Ponsonby and asked me imperiously if I wanted her ram. Obviously, I thought this was someone making a rather funny rural joke and replied with a terse no. In this rash moment I deprived our sheep of their only opportunity of excitement in their lives [apart from being dipped and deloused]. Had it not been for me, they could have been spending long illicit afternoons of sin with the Warren Beatty of the cloven-hooved set.

It was a long time before Lady Ponsonby got back in touch but her ram eventually became a regular visitor. We couldn't stand the thought of any more bottom-poking in the paddock in the wee hours of the morning. But no matter how many urgent calls out to the lambing shed I get, I would never get rid of our sheep. Lambs herald the spring with a delicious freshness, and besides they're very picturesque.

'I'm bored with my life,' said Honey. 'Bored with clothes, bored with foreign travel. The only thing I'm not bored with is poetry.'

In order to stem this fit of ennui, I took the children out to the paddock to see the lambs. We swung on the gate, singing a selection from *The Sound of Music* which was currently very much in vogue at our house. It is a musical that holds many happy memories for me of Harmony's childhood, because when she first saw it at the age of three she became obsessed with nuns. A friend who has a cousin who is a nun finally invited her to go and visit on the nuns' annual day—a very special day as the nuns were only allowed to speak once every year. Harmony was bundled into the car, my friend armed with her video camera, and when they arrived all the nuns had formed a neat circle in the visitors' room in order to admire Harmony, and sing with her 'The Hills are Alive with the Sound of Music' and 'Dominica Nica Nica', which every good nun has in her repertoire.

Unfortunately, out of nowhere Harmony suddenly broke off from her perch on a stool in the middle of the room and, fixing my friend with a tenacious stare, asked, 'What does *massive* mean?' [She's always been unexpected.]

The nuns paused, their heads on one side, eyebrows raised expectantly. The video camera wobbled slightly as a frisson of fear ran through my friend's veins.

'It means big, Harmony,' she replied.

'Oh,' said Harmony, 'I thought it must do because Mummy always says massive penis.'

At this, the nuns broke wildly into song again, and the incident was closed for a year until they could discuss it with each other again.

As the children and I walked towards home, we saw a youth approaching us. He was wearing black leather biker's boots and studded trousers encased his muscular, rather stocky legs, while a peaked leather cap was placed at a jaunty sideways angle on his head. 'Yo!' he shouted, winking gamely at Lowther who was trimming some ivy. Lowther looked suitably bewildered at this greeting and replied, 'Ar!'

'Hello,' I said, noticing that my voice had gone rather like the Queen Mother's, as I was talking through a mouth like a hen's bottom. 'Can we help you at all?'

'Yup, I'm Cedric. I've just moved in over the way,' he replied, his earrings glittering in the sunlight. I could see the outline of another ring through his nipple under his rather unseasonably thin shirt. He went on to explain that he worked for the hairdresser Nigel de Canterbury, and was new to Compton Pauncefoot. In a bid to become part of the town's community, he said he'd even taken the drastic step of joining the Fete Committee. 'I can't wait to attend your meetings,' continued my new friend. 'We're all in such close proximity and it would be heaven to get to know you all better.'

I accepted an offer to pop round for tea, and he swung off back home. At the main gates he paused and bellowed 'Ciao then, Bella!' over one shoulder and then broke into a little trot across the main road.

I heard Lowther humphing from his perch up the ladder.

'Did that man have another ear on his chest, Mum?' asked Honey. It was time for another crumpet.

CHAPTER 3

Love Is In The Air

'THE TROUBLE WITH MEN in Compton Paunce-foot,' moaned Dorcas Plant wanly, 'is that they won't commit to buying a combine harvester on hire purchase, let alone to a lasting relationship with someone beautiful and caring like ... well, like me for example.'

My friend Dorcas Plant was renting the flat across the road since her marriage to Plant the upholsterer broke up when they had a violent quarrel and he trapped her nose in the airing cupboard door, blacking both her eyes. Dorcas is thirtysomething, pink, plump and over-sexed, but enjoys monumental self-confidence which makes her very appealing. She is determined not to stay single for much longer.

We had just bumped into each other in the Market Square and were now walking up the High Street to the

Honeypot café for some of their steamingly delicious tea and cakes. It was a very cold day; a brutal wind blew down the street like a wind tunnel and kept blowing Dorcas's rather short skirt up to expose a shiny pair of red knickers. Despite the cold, Dorcas was sporting a short, rather flimsy, floral dress [which meant she had blue mottly legs], high-heeled court shoes, and a wide open pale blue tweed coat, with a fox-foot brooch on one lapel.

As we got nearer to the café she offered to demonstrate how she radiated sex now she was single again. Intrigued, I insisted on a demonstration. She did it for four steps and three local boys walked into the bottle bank outside the town hall! I tried to analyse what she did when she was radiating sex, but apart from expertly emulating the facial expressions of someone starring in a particularly harrowing haemorrhoid cream commercial, I couldn't put my finger on the intangible something she possessed. Then I tried radiating sex, and the man on the fruit stall outside the Nat West shouted, 'Don't worry love, it may never happen.' Which was annoying.

With her chubby pink and purple legs and her tiny feet encased in their little shoes looking like trotters, Dorcas had to run to keep up even with me, and I'm a pygmy, I thought bitterly.

'I keep telling you,' she muttered from about ten feet behind me. 'I'm just a sizzler, I'm simply wasted on men down here.' I pondered on what it must be like to have such incredibly high self-esteem, but tripped on a loose paving stone.

It is hard to be a single woman in the rural areas of

this green and pleasant land. All the men are definitely shyer, there aren't so many of them and they are also permanently tired. Most of the men in our area still farm and get up at four, so, if they take you on a date, by eight o'clock at night they're desperate for bed. There are also not so many opportunities to meet, unlike London or other big smokes—the occasional grim disco with four bike lamps flashing from the top of a barn, the possibility of joining the local thespian group and French and Spanish classes at night school at the tech are hardly events brimming with suppressed passions.

Maybe it's also because farmers traditionally spend their time like the actors do on *All Creatures Great and Small,* pulling animals out of their mothers with the aid of two ropes and a big winch, so that their attitude to sex is less than sexy. Sirens in Compton Pauncefoot are a dying breed, the idea of lying in louche splendour in front of a roaring log fire meaningfully rubbing the head of a well-stuffed lion skin seems rather a waste of time when you're directing your potent allure at someone who is trying to avoid dropping off to sleep by concentrating on chipping some pig poo off his wellington boot.

As far as talking dirty goes, three hours discussing farm subsidies and the water shortage can leave a girl yearning for an opium den and a few verses of Coleridge. Dorcas is always telling me that for her the hardest part of being the local sexy siren is making sure that no one finds out what she is really like at home, when she sits around on the sofa eating Ready Brek watching *Blind Date* looking like one of the lesbian serial killers on *Prisoner—Cell Block H.*

So there are a number of problems she faces in trying to get married. The main one is the shortage of eligible bachelors, and the second being the fact that they aren't as glamorous as Dorcas would like them to be. She longs for something more, someone with a pair of flashing eyes, a chiselled jaw, a sort of walking, talking, constructivist statue ...

The Honeypot is very successful, even though last year it changed hands and everyone thought it would never be the same again, and that it might lose its olde worlde charme which attracts tourists from as far away as Oare. It still serves coffees, teas, Welsh rarebit and chocolate horns to exhausted shoppers, tired of choosing between tripe and kidneys at the butcher next-door. The two Australians who became the new proprietors have tried to give it a more cosmopolitan air—they have added a large red and white striped awning and a big chrome frame to keep the wind off everyone sitting at the four new tables, which are actually on the pavement in the market place as you find in Gay Paree.

Having said that, the High Street in Compton Pauncefoot is not much of a catwalk. All last summer we waited for summer, and now we were spending all spring waiting for a bit of spring weather. With the ill-fated optimism of pilgrims we sat outside the Honeypot shivering expectantly, but the weather stayed unforgivingly sharp. As we walked towards the café today, it became apparent that as usual it was packed almost to bursting point with shoppers, and no one likes to look like they are lurking around waiting for a seat outside.

I pulled my jacket around myself and huddled in the doorway. I tried to look like I was waiting for someone, not a seat. I also attempted to peer at my red nose in the chrome bar holding up the awnings. A large lady clutching a huge sack of swedes saw me and smirked. Then I pretended I was looking past the chrome tube and not actually into it. Dorcas was still in Boots, so I was all alone in my vigil for a pair of empty chairs!

Soon a local housewife and her rather spotty son left [he was attempting to look modishly vacant I noticed]. I tried to act as if I wasn't pushing in, and lunged at the empty seats. There was a brief scuffle with two large matronly types also feigning complete indifference but obviously palpitating at the thought of a large hot chocolate slightly sheltered from the biting wind.

Behind us the warm interior of the café was packed. The waitresses wore overcoats and kept up a steady stream of fragrant tea to the walking wounded struggling in with their laden baskets. By the time Dorcas wiggled in, eight of us were crammed around a small circular table. She punched the air jubilantly when she saw my success at securing our chairs and a large plate of buns and cakes. Then she pushed her large behind down beside me, proclaiming 'Shove over Marigold' to the woman on her right in ringing, rather Sloanie tones despite her claim that she is a 'Maid of Kent' as locals proudly put it.

Dorcas peered around for any eligible men, but they

were probably all hard at work in the fields, where at this time of year they spend their time ploughing wide furrows in last year's stubble. 'Anyway,' said Dorcas, 'I want glamour, not someone with all the dashing charms of a fluff-covered Everton Mint.'

I mentioned that in order to be really dashing it also helps if you're not terminally afflicted by timidity. Dorcas claims this is a problem for much of the agricultural community, although I think it's something to do with the fact that she even Hoovers in the nude. Because of the shyness of many in the area, an intriguing new addition to the High Street has been the Tahitian Friendly Society above the sweet shop. Here shy farmers can get themselves married to beautiful Tahitian girls who then long for more glamour and dump them for men in Staines. Dorcas wondered if they could fix her up with someone nice if she went for a few sunbed treatments in Canterbury, but I pointed out that she was already on the list of the Cathedral Lonely Hearts Dating Agency.

'Oh Gord,' she trilled. 'They sent me on a date last week, and when I arrived he was four feet tall and wearing a pink leather pork pie hat. He was a holistic dentist on a sabbatical from Rotorua and told me he was a direct descendant of the Giant Clam. I really do have the worst luck in this sort of thing.'

At that moment a vision approached, standing out amongst all the ladies with baskets and small children. It was Cedric, splendidly attired in ripped jeans and a tee-shirt that said *I'M WITH STUPID*.

'Hello,' he said.

'Hello handsome,' Dorcas replied, laughing loudly at

her own joke which she invariably does. Her laugh is truly unmistakable, trilling OOOOOOAAAAAAG-HHHH in a short, sharp ascending scale. Her massively glorious pink bosom wobbled vigorously.

'Crikey,' I heard a small boy intone behind her.

At first sight, Cedric seemed very good-looking, but if you looked at him for too long you suddenly noticed that everything was on crooked and his ears were a bit like stained-glass jug handles. I can't sleep in my bed if the curtains are crooked so Cedric's ears bothered me a lot. Cedric told us about himself. He is not the usual young man you meet in Compton Pauncefoot. He seems to have a heart like a bus, and said he liked kissing everyone, although he drew the line at people who were throwing up at the time. Dorcas knew that, before switching to hairdressing, he had apparently studied art mainly because the studio was the only room at the tech in Canterbury where the heating worked really well.

'Gosh,' she said, looking serious and dramatic. 'How these grey February skies remind one of Canaletto.'

Cedric looked up, squinted, and burped. 'Yeah,' he said. 'Like wicked.'

I leaned back and smelt the air. It was redolent with the various smells of the market place, mingling with steamy cappuccino and Cedric's aftershave. I could also smell the pungent aroma of Dorcas's new anti-cellulite cream which she had informed me was an extract of underground roots. Actually it smells exactly like something that would squirt at high velocity out of a snuffling nocturnal animal. She also tells me it leaves a residue all over the bath so that it's like sitting in a concrete mixer.

I became suddenly claustrophobic, and shifted myself to get a little more space in which to eat my third cream slice, but Dorcas shifted too, making an attempt at flirting with Cedric before he went round to visit the Vicar for a cup of tea. I thought it was pointless. The last time she went round to Cedric's she'd performed her party piece which consists of pulling a Durex over her head and inflating it with her nostrils—hardly the sort of seductive trick you can imagine Jerry Hall using on oil barons—and left Cedric looking dazed.

But Cedric reached over to sip Dorcas's hot chocolate and slipped. The cup shot upwards and there was a terrible yelp.

'Ohhh, I'm scalded,' Dorcas screeched.

'Wow,' said Cedric, stuck between two old ladies and a trolley.

'You big idiot,' said Dorcas.

'I'm so sorry,' said poor Cedric.

'Get me some water, soda water, NOT BADOIT, I hate Badoit,' Dorcas was bellowing at a waitress who had no idea what she was talking about. Cedric tried to dab ineffectually at the spreading stain with a corner of his leather jacket, his cool demeanour momentarily but publicly shaken. He bravely attempted an insouciant smile and rushed off towards the chip shop.

On the way home I could hear her thighs rubbing together as her skirt stuck to them, soaked with coffee and chocolate. Then, outside the fishing-tackle shop, she spotted a machine measuring your sex appeal when you stick your index finger through a hole. She did so and it shot straight off the scale. She looked at me a trifle smugly and tripped off home reasonably happy again. I didn't try it out as I didn't need to be told I was a halibut.

When I arrived home, Harmony and Honey were painting in the kitchen. Heavenly wasn't but she was silently and determinedly swirling a brush full of blue paint in her sister's ear, Harmony with her tongue hanging out slightly trying to paint a blue thrush egg she'd just found broken on the grass.

By early March all the birds around here feel in the mood for love and start acting like Dorcas. The trees in the fields near to local photographer Brian's house are filled with rookeries. Preparing to have families, each rook is very concerned about nest building and is somehow able to identify every twig in his nest, so that if a neighbour attempts to steal one for a new bathroom or spare bedroom annexe all hell lets loose until the twig is duly returned.

My own favourites are the hedge sparrows, simply because I admire anyone who uses dance to attract a mate. [I am to dancing, sadly, what Bernard Manning is to the body-stocking.] Hedge sparrows each have their own little dance as a form of love-making and flap around in the woods at the end of our garden making their beautiful song—no surprise as they are the cousins of the nightingale.

Just as I was watching the girls finish their painting, and suggesting that perhaps we should go for a nature walk to look for twigs, feathers or maybe even a fallen nest, I heard a cacophony of hooting outside. I decided to investigate immediately in case it was someone new who might become fatally attracted to me even though I was wearing Emerson Fittipaldi's boilersuit, fetchingly teamed with two slightly rusty kirby-grips on either side of my parting.

Outside stood a beautiful gleaming vintage car, with a fully liveried chauffeur standing to attention holding open the back door which had a family crest with the motto *Semper ad Lucem* twining around the knob.

In the back of the car I could dimly make out a large fuzzy black and white Jacob's ram. Its horns were well polished and curled around twice and its eyes glittered; it could have auditioned for a starring roll in a Dennis Wheatley film, circa 1972. As he stood up, his little tartan car rug falling to the floor of the car, I realised that this was the glamorous stranger come to make my sheep feel like new women.

I'd forgotten Lady Ponsonby had called me the day before. She always talks incredibly loudly and reminds me of English people on holiday on the Continent who always think that simply adding decibels is the equivalent of a two-year Berlitz course. Alternatively they add an O to the end of everything they say and can be heard bellowing 'More HOTTO' to waiters when they are getting their morning tea.

'Do you want the ram to come over? Squires will be free to bring him tomorrow afternoon, if you need his services again for your gals,' yelled Lady P.

I'd said yes, and weakly plucked a dead head off a geranium.

We all stood solemnly in a welcoming committee in order of height. Starting with Lowther, and ending with Heavenly and the dog, who was feeling bilious after eating a tin of old beans out of the neighbours' bin bag.

The ram gave a little leap out of the car and pulled around at the paddock, perhaps sizing up the talent. He was obviously a legend in his own feeding trough because the minute the sheep saw him they all bleated furiously, scattered and hid in the nettles on the other side of the garden.

Having spent the morning watching Dorcas perform her courtship dance [up to the moment she was doused with hot chocolate], I watched as our guest ambled his way nonchalantly across the field before, without any more delay, he lunged madly at the first sheep and without any fuss began his hard day's work. I wished that it could all be so easy for Dorcas. Thinking of her I decided to go round to see how she was. I found her perched on the side of the bath, swishing a pair of knickers around in Bio-Tex, sniffing. It was an unusual sight—even as a child she started the Happy Club because she was always in a good mood, and extorted money out of her four sisters if they weren't.

Trying to cheer her up, I listed a lot of much worse things that could be happening to her. She could be stuck in a toilet cubicle at a nightclub in downtown Canterbury, listening to two sixteen-year-old sexpots outside discussing how fat she was. She could be at one of the Lord Mayor's cheese and wine parties when he gets in a group of Lithuanian performance artists to discuss Freedom of the Press and how it affects the Medway. Dorcas began to feel better, even if she was still single. She took off her knickers and began to Nair her bikini line, then described in horrible detail an article she'd been reading in *Horse and Pony* about 'The Rise of the Pony Club'. Dorcas, in her exhaustingly optimistic view of life, found all of that 'very beneficial really'.

She then remembered she had a *massive* item of news to tell me—she thought Daniel Day-Lewis was renting a holiday cottage nearby. She was walking home from a baby shower at one of the farms near the Priory the other night and swore she saw a spectral vision of Daniel Day-Lewis outside the only Indian restaurant in Compton Pauncefoot. I said it was obviously a drunken vision sent to torture her after a night spent with peers who are not only married but pregnant too. Dorcas admitted that they'd discussed stretch marks, the terrible stains that fertiliser made on overalls and how to get rid of them, and how sensitively Richard Clayderman played on his new CD. Dorcas had finally stomped off saying she thought that he was a big girl's blouse and the only thing CDs were good for was doing your hair in the reflection.

Anyway, on the way home she insisted she saw him. This had also been confirmed by Mr Luigi, our local dry cleaner—he is prone to revealing things. He'd been cleaning the Day-Lewis duvet cover and now he was acting like he was 'By Royal Appointment' and thinking of putting up his rates for a pleated skirt. Personally, I hardly think it's the Golden Age of Hollywood when our premier young actor sleeps under an orange and tan floral duvet cover bought in a flood damage sale at Dickens and Jones.

Dorcas said she had convinced Mr Luigi that she was in fact a budding thespian herself, rather than a slavering beauty on the hunting trail of romance. She claimed she was about to play the juvenile lead in *Kismet*; the mouthwatering thought of Dorcas completely filling a pair of flimsy pink nylon harem pants while her ample bosom heaved around like two gorgonzolas fighting for freedom loosened his tongue, so that it's now been arranged that her party dress is going to be stuffed into the Day-Lewis duvet cover to see if they'll mate, or at least if he'll bring it back.

Dorcas threw herself back on to the sofa and looked at the cottage garden prints hung randomly and squiffily everywhere. 'He's bound to return my dress because he went to a public school and that teaches a man to respect women and have very good manners.'

And other things I think, but remain politely silent. Harmony then raced in to tell me that Honey had tied the rabbit spread-eagled to the bed with two skipping ropes and was hyperventilating. I couldn't find out which one of them was hyperventilating so I had to leave dear Dorcas dreaming.

Dorcas spent the following three weeks in almost complete darkness. Her sitting room began to resemble the Odeon as she sat watching *The Bounty* and *My Left Foot* continuously. By the time she finally gave *The Bounty* back to the video shop in town, she could have made several sequels with the overtime they charged her. The only other time so much money was spent in one go was when Dorcas lost *The Great Gatsby* down the back of the sofa for three months.

Every time I called round to see her she was lying on the sofa with a bag of sweets on her chest, chewing and staring wistfully at Day-Lewis's chiselled features.

Halfway through my sixth *Left Foot*, we were in the middle of a cup of tea, and I had opened the curtains and the windows to try and fumigate the room as the dog had been at the wine gums again, when Dorcas suddenly leaped up and said that she was late for her appointment with Errol. I couldn't remember who Errol was, although I remembered hearing his name before, but she told me to stay put and watch the rest of the film, and she'd soon be back. I'd just settled myself on to the bergère with a cup of fruit punch when there was a forceful knock at her front door.

It was him, in all his glory, standing on the front doorstep, clutching Dorcas's party dress as if it were a specimen jar in a fertility clinic.

'I think I accidentally got your dress in my duvet cover,' he said, a lock of dark hair falling over one smouldering brown eye. He looked very much like the pirate hero of *Love's Tender Loins* which I was currently rereading in bed at night.

'No, no, no,' I replied in a funny falsetto voice that I'd suddenly acquired. 'That belongs to my beautiful, talented neighbour who will be back soon.'

In times of stress I like to be loyal, but the next problem was how to get a major movie star with a sequined dress to stay. I hoped I hadn't sounded too effusive about Dorcas; he probably thought I was going out with her now. So I added, 'It's a size fourteen.'

Looking shifty, he came in and I told him that Dorcas

would never forgive herself if she didn't personally thank him. Once he was in the gloomy interior of Dorcas's dining room, I handed him a fruit punch and desperately tried to break the ice by telling him that Dorcas and I had been so mortified with embarrassment during the sexy bits in *My Beautiful Launderette* we'd had to take the cover off the spare bed and put it over our heads on his behalf. He looked at his watch. I hoped Dorcas would do better than me.

He told me he'd run over from his place, which was about eight miles away. I immediately imagined him skipping winsomely along the tow path like a male Isadora Duncan, his long hair flying, cheekbones cutting through the breeze like razors, lips pouting at passing patches of mignonette. He looked at his watch and I stared nervously at his crotch because I simply couldn't look him in the eye, although this is something I never did until I got to know Dorcas.

Just as he started to stare down to see if his flies were undone, Dorcas walked in. Handing her the steaming cup of tea I had just made to give me something to do while we sat there like two lemons, I briefly introduced them both. She sat there with her tea, and as she sipped it the liquid slid out of the corner of her mouth and trickled down towards her bosom, and then vanished from view into her cleavage. I watched mesmerised. She appeared totally unaware of what was happening. I glanced at Daniel Day-Lewis who was staring intently at her.

'Do tell me what you're working on next,' I trilled.

He didn't reply. He was still gazing at Dorcas, rapt,

watching the spreading brown tea stain soaking into her organdie bodice.

Dorcas then started to do something strange with her top lip and nose, not unlike the gyrations of a very bad Elvis Presley impersonator having an off night at Batley Variety Club. She blew a large bubble of spit out of the side of her mouth. I had to hand it to her—she certainly knew how to get a man's complete attention.

'I may join the National,' he said, still not taking his eyes off Dorcas. The silence was almost too much to bear, and Dorcas reached for a chocolate bourbon biscuit which she repeatedly tried to insert into her cheek. Finally, she got it into her mouth and with a final desperate attempt at looking seductive she took a big swig of tea, choked violently, and a chunk of biscuit flew out of her nose.

'What's the matter with you?' I said, driven to this by the horror of the last few minutes, although Daniel seemed totally engrossed. But I didn't want him to think she was always like this, did I? Dorcas was pitifully wiping wet biscuit off her chest.

'I've jush comsh from the dentish. I hadsh to hash a jabsh, and I didn't know he was gon be here dish I?'

There was a pause, as she dabbed at her nose. 'I hadsh to have a jabsh,' she spluttered across the room.

Dorcas's big moment of rural passion had been destroyed by one small injection in the gum from her dentist Errol. There was nothing to be done about it, even though Daniel told several stories about humiliating things he'd done under anaesthetics, and I repeated a story about my granny unzipping the dentist's flies after some sodium pentathol.

Finally, he stood up to go. I have to admit that he's obviously a truly great actor because he looked just like Rhett Butler as he stood next to the spin dryer in the laundry room with both of Dorcas's plump spit-stained cheeks in his hands, looking deeply into her eyes.

'You're a dish,' he added. For a second I thought he was imitating her speech impediment, but he wasn't. 'I'll never forget you,' he murmured and ran off down Priory Road without looking back.

Dorcas turned around, ran upstairs to her bedroom, threw herself on to the bed and pulled a bottle of Malibu from under the bed and took a big swig. I handed her three Valium. When she was just about to go to sleep, possibly forever, she sat up on the bed.

'I hearsh there'sh a new boysh at the hop farmsh,' she spat, before falling backwards on to the duvet with her eyes tightly shut.

I went home, and put the girls to bed—they all sleep in one big bed a bit like the Seven Dwarfs. I read them a story and patted their little pink sweet faces, and told them we'd go and see one of the local farmers milking his cows the next day.

CHAPTER 4

The Vicar

Even before he arrived at the pretty little church of St Perbold's, there were rumblings in the pews about the new vicar. His 'Roman' leanings had been heard of and much discussed, as were his strong beliefs about allowing pets in church during services, his E-type Jag, and his occasional visits to discos in Whitstable. Compton Pauncefoot prided itself on being devoutly Low Church, so much so that the verger left when the new vicar was about to arrive because he couldn't bear the thought of vestments and trimmings. And there were no doubts in the mind of the curate that this was going to be a vicar who utilised the fifteen-fold amen, did more genuflecting than the Winter Olympics and would be holding his services tarted up like an Anglican Cher.

Once the Vicar did arrive the congregation could

hardly sing for sniffing the air surreptitiously for the merest whiff of incense, which they were convinced he was going to leak into the services like dry ice on *Top of the Pops*, distracting everyone from the one God and possibly causing heathen dancing to break out in the back row. All of a sudden matins sounded like the training school for Heathrow Airport tracker dogs.

Damning evidence of a leaning towards the papacy finally came from the Vicar's own daily woman, a young lady called Mrs Hill who actually comes from Essex and has married three local farmers in quick succession, exhausting all of them with her love of rubber clothing. Once she had infiltrated the Vicar's inner sanctum, so to speak, clutching his Hoover and wearing what appeared to him to be an inner tyre, she lost no time in reporting to everyone at Earl Spencer's Slug Pellet that the Vicar had a souvenir plate 'UP ON THE WALL' in the kitchenette—depicting the Pope, John F. Kennedy and Barry McGuigan in a glorious technicolour triumvirate against the back drop of St Paul's Basilica.

Since he first chugged up the hill in his shiny red car, battles have surrounded his every move—at some point I suspect that Hollywood may get on the phone interested in the film rights to his story.

Millicent came over to borrow a jug of sherry for a trifle she was making to celebrate the anniversary of the invention of the lava lamp, which I pointed out wasn't for several months, so she sat down at the kitchen table and drank it instead. She was looking as beautiful as ever, albeit a little faded at the edges, a fascinating marriage between Alistair Sim and Simone Signoret (if they both wore red wigs).

She waved her lilac Russian cocktail cigarette which was firmly stuffed into a foot-long diamanté-trimmed holder, so firmly that it was bent almost at right angles to the holder. She was waving in the direction of the church, which is actually a part of our house although in constant working order. At that point the sounds of evensong drifted into the kitchen, filling it with music and appalling singing. 'Heard the latest?' she said so loudly I was convinced the congregation would think it was part of the Vicar's sermon. 'About his bloody tea urn?' she hissed.

'Everyone is absolutely up in arms—no one can agree when he should switch the blasted thing on you see. Of course the tea urn is just part of the whole picture if you ask me, the broader issues—first he introduced all that ghastly clapping, then he made the choir beam all the time. Half of them look like they've had strychnine. And then all those dreadful hymns, like 'Dance, dance, wherever you may be' and Cliff Richard's Christmas hits. And finally, the tea urn. It makes such a noise while it's boiling up that he has to bellow the sermon over the top of what sounds like that groaning nonsense of 'Je t'aime'. But there's not much choice. Either it goes on during the sermon, which sounds like someone's trying to film a porno movie in the vestry, or it goes on right at the end and everyone has to wait twenty minutes for their tea and Pot Noodles at the end of the service. Personally, I feel he should decide if it's a place of worship or a Little Chef!'

Millicent paused for breath, stabbing the air with the bent cigarette. This was not the first of these altercations to arise. The one about the changes to the 'fabric of the church' was still brewing. Other local vicars, all of them chums of our own dear vicar, longed to spend their bits of fete money on having the thatch replaced over the churchyard gate, or having a bit of calligraphy tarted up, but our vicar wanted a power shower. He'd seen the ones in our house—the ones used previously to break up Indian riots—and now he wanted a lilac one in the church. 'Not that it would stop there of course. Next it will be shagpile altar mats and gold swan-shaped font knobs, I can tell you.' She paused for breath again, lighting another cigarette and adding some cherry brandy out of her flask to her tea.

'An' it's no use thinking I'm being unfair. I've heard from Mrs Hill what the vicarage is like. He's got a pale blue plastic quilted toilet seat that plays the "Marseillaise" when you lift up the toilet seat. A man like that would positively love an organ covered in more flashing lights than a jungle landing strip. It's no good trying to pacify me. The way he's got the vicarage tricked up—so unvicarly, all that gilt—it looks like he's copied a knocking shop in Cleethorpes. By the way—have you noticed how Violet Sourbutt looks exactly like a dachshund from behind when she's kneeling down for communion?'

Then I noticed that Honey was entirely piebald-coloured. Harmony had apparently spent the time I'd been chatting industriously painting her sister using some arcane form of chemical warfare consisting of three Q-tips and an old bottle of Tanfastic she'd unearthed from under the sink.

'Anyway, did his cleaner tell you about his plate?' asked Millicent.

'No,' I replied. 'She came over to see if I needed any help with the house—I fell down on the ground kissing her feet and that halted the conversation a bit, but she's coming in three mornings a week, starting next week.'

'Well, must be going. Honey really looks rather pretty striped like that, rather like a young zebra roaming the plains, dontchathink? Or maybe it's a baboon's backside she's reminding me of. See you at the fete committee meeting later.'

Not everyone felt so hostile towards the Vicar. The unobtainable being notoriously attractive, I felt all my single friends could ask him for tips on how to radiate sex if he had a few free moments after matins. Everyone knows that spinsters, elderly ladies in raincoats and very bored housewives are always getting wildly attracted to their vicar, especially if he has a lift-and-separate posing pouch, quilted toilet seats and an E-type Jag in the drive. It only adds to the spice of life that he's somewhat unavailable.

Look at all the other people who are furiously desirable. Dr Kildare was a heart-throb because he was a doctor who, like vicars, are ripe for community crushes. Catholic priests are even sexier than vicars, of course, because they're totally unobtainable. Everyone was gripped by *The Thorn Birds* on the telly because that was about a glorious girl who fell in love with a Catholic priest who was played by Dr Kildare which made the whole thing triply enchantingly thrilling. Montgomery Clift in *I Confess* was perfect for fantasies, except that he's dead too, though I suppose you can't get much more unobtainable than that, can you?

So our vicar finds himself completely inundated with invitations to supper, requests for exorcisms and offers of soaps on ropes for the future shower unit. Plus, I hear, he frequently finds delicious jam tarts and huge marrows left anonymously on his doorstep.

At three o'clock that afternoon I locked the children out in the garden with a picnic hamper of astonishing proportions crammed with everything the Honeypot had to offer. Honey was wearing a shower cap with a tea towel tied firmly around it to stop her flick-ups going limp outside. I instructed her as firmly as possible not to do anything else to the rabbit that day, as earlier on I'd had to persuade her against the tonsillectomy she'd been contemplating for the poor thing as that afternoon's entertainment.

Heavenly was throwing herself off the mounting stairs, then lying on the ground saying, 'Look Mummy, I'm dead, like Juliet in the play,' which I was impressed by as it sounded so clever from someone the size of a chip.

Harmony was racing through the undergrowth with her friends Simon and Tom, all shouting 'Pow! Pow!' loudly and firing at each other with courgettes.

Husband was lying on a car rug in the garden under the huge lemony magnolia, reading Pepys's *Diaries* and eating fig rolls.

All was well in the world it seemed to me.

As soon as I arrived at the vicarage it was apparent that all did not seem so well in the world to the poor Vicar. He was standing looking quite forlorn in the middle of the vicarage's small but perfectly co-ordinated sitting room in a pair of pale salmon hipster flares and a polo-neck skinny rib jumper, which he's obviously had since the first time they were both fashionable. His winkle-toe Chelsea boots shone but he was obviously not a happy man.

The room was very hot, and furnished entirely in different sorts of tartan, with many dangling tassles and a multitude of small ornaments from all over the world jostling for space on spindly Louis-Quatorze tables.

On one stool perched Cedric in his usual sexy avant-garde clothes. A fire burned merrily in the grate so that he'd been forced to remove his heavy studded leather jacket.

Millicent perched archly on a little chair with a crowded plate of cakes. Sue had hopped into her car and driven over and sat next to her talking about their death watch beetles, wearing a huge hooped gingham skirt, and a large picture hat which kept poking Millicent in the eye. She is my greatest friend. With her exquisite taste she is Kent's answer to Cecil Beaton; she's also a keen follower of all things New Age. Her husband Perce had decided not to come and instead had gone off round his own garden enjoying the peace.

Crammed on to an ornate but small chaise-longue were the two Australian proprietors of the Honeypot, Des and Desirée from Sydney chatting animatedly to Brian, the photographer. As well as photographing all our most important local events like the inauguration of the new mayor, he owns a villa on the Costa del Sol, and is a great Hispanophile and teaches Spanish at the tech. He wears a cape for photographing all the best local weddings but at the tech makes do teaching students to make paella, tie a mantilla and say 'My war wound is aching on the sideboard' in five different dialects.

He even made it into the local paper, although that had nothing to do with either Spain or his photography, but a row with the local farmer whose land backs on to both his and Millicent's houses. Plagued with birds eating his seeds, he installed a new high-tech device. Replacing the scarecrow of olden times, it fired an incredibly noisy fourteen-pellet salute into the air every half hour. The regularity of these noise assaults slowly began to send Brian mad, and as soon as he complained the farmer increased the noise pollution to one every fifteen minutes.

Finally, one morning as he ate his breakfast, Brian spotted the farmer adjusting his timer in the field, and, insane with anger, overturned the table and ran out into the field, wearing a smoking jacket, cravat and no trousers, much to Millicent's delight.

Unfortunately the matron of the old people's home to their right complained that the sight of Brian's trim thighs throbbing past the conservatory windows had caused three old ladies to need bed rest and the scandal hit the *Kent Messenger* with a thud all across the front page!

Two elderly sisters called Abby and Violet Sourbutt, dressed perfectly in floral frocks and wizened cardigans, completed the scene, hovering next to the fire with cups of tea. The Vicar seemed to relax after the cakes were doled out; he flitted in and out of the kitchenette giving everyone tantalising glimpses of the papal plate on the wall. It was obvious that the Vicar liked to preside over a sumptuous tea—it was all most gracious. A marvellous array of Honeypot cakes—Victoria sponges, home-made scones, Swiss rolls, gingerbread biscuits and shortbread petticoat tails—lay at his feet. In between the two elderly spinsters a little silver kettle sang and steamed away on a spirit stove.

Though the rural year is punctuated predictably at preordained moments charmingly though erroneously called 'events', nothing is more imperative for our household than the annual church fete. Although such moments are the staple of the canon of country life literature, the cliché is all too justified, for it is at this village knees-up that the passions, rivalries and politics, the adulteries, romances and plain bitchiness come to the fore, usually and traditionally under the baleful eye of the midsummer sun.

This tea is the moment when, as owners of the Priory, we formally receive our long advance notice of the fete, to be followed by the annual letter from the annual 'chair' requesting the use of the paddock. Just in case we are thinking the unthinkable and refusing the formulaic permission, we are reminded discreetly how every owner since Eldred the Unsteady has granted this annual boon, so it is really nothing to do with us anyway. It is the fete's right by ancient ritual.

This year it seemed that the Vicar had his mind on subjects more important than whether two bands of morris dancers might be too much, and should the entrance price be upped this year to thirty pence? It was obvious he had to get something off his chest before discussions of the gate could follow harmoniously.

'When we were at theological college,' the Vicar murmured, 'we were taught that when we performed a funeral at a crematorium we must always, always, check to discover exactly where the coffin would leave the catafalque. Of course, dears, it was for two very important reasons. Firstly, the disappearance of the coffin is often the most distressing and traumatic moment for the bereaved, the last sight of their loved ones, so one has to be able to tell them what to expect, when it will move and where it will go when it disappears completely.

'The other reason is that sometimes the priest is the one who must activate the mechanism which causes the coffin to move ...,' the Vicar paused and blew a smoke ring dramatically into Violet's expectant face. 'This morning I took a funeral, and discovered not only that I did not have to move the mechanism but also that the coffin didn't move immediately—some blue curtains swept into place, hiding it from view, and it then went down on to a lift. When the service started, by some hideous accident I was on the wrong side of the curtains,

72

so they suddenly swept around me obscuring me from view, as I bellowed the prayers like an announcer on a very bad game show, before I was lowered very cere-moniously and agonisingly slowly into the bowels of the building where I found a caretaker asleep next to a cage of ferrets. I finally came back up and the coffin had vanished away forever and I suddenly remembered seeing Marlene Dietrich once take a curtain call. She folded herself into the curtain in a particularly sensuous way, finally pushing it back, making mean little rippling movements with her hands which I emulated as best I could, although it wasn't that easy in my robes. I don't think I was as successful as Marlene because when I finally did reappear from behind the deep blue velvet, a woman in the front row shrieked and had to be lead out sobbing. And then, like a pantomime, the blasted coffin came back up again too.'

The Vicar subsided back into his armchair, visibly upset by his morning's traumatic turn of events, so sad that even the mortally anti-papist Millicent turned to Cedric to discuss a glorious golden chasuble she'd seen recently in a shop in Tunbridge Wells that she felt would suit the Vicar perfectly.

Cedric, cheered by this thought and ever the enthu-siastic newcomer, mentioned that it was almost time for the fete committee to convene. Had anyone got any inspired ideas for a theme?

Since I've moved to the country I like to think that I've embraced some of the great traditions of country living. I've made crab apple jelly with all the alluring consistency of a bad attack of molten lava, I long for

73

our first body in the library, and I have reacquainted myself with the joys of amateur dramatics.

It was this subject that was raising its head at tea that afternoon, because this year, in order to think BIG, some members of the committee thought that a variety show in the illegal Nissen hut at Teynham was exactly what was needed to add a bit of stardust to the proceedings. It was patently obvious that the Vicar and Brian didn't agree at all, especially the Vicar who was in a tetchy sensitive mood anyway.

'What kind of show exactly?' enquired Millicent archly, obviously imagining herself in a Noel Coward play. She had once performed the role of Scheherazade with the Women's Circle, dancing around a small Bunsen burner which was doubling as the campfire. She wore gold hooped earrings, a shawl and a lot of sooty eye make-up and banged her tambourine constantly, casting a lot of deeply meaningful glances at the Archbishop who attended the opening night. It appears that as her tambourining reached fever pitch she felt that she had missed her true vocation as an understudy to Liza Minnelli.

Abby pointed out that she thought a variety show gave everyone a chance to display their individual talents.

'It seems to me if we did it one person would have to take charge,' noted her little sister Violet so forcefully she toppled backwards on to the sofa with her small sparrow-thin legs in the air.

Surprisingly it was Sue, exquisite, lovely, spiritual Sue who can most often be found holding seances in her

cricket pavilion, who had the most experience of amateur drama of any kind. Despite the fact that she is so
spiritual she makes the Dalai Lama look like a lager lout,
she was once persuaded to join the Mid-Kent Players in
their summer production of *Doctor in the House*. Although Sue is always dressed as though she's about to
perform several rousing choruses of *The Mikado*, and
lives in a vast Gothic pile filled with marvellous objects
like tartan dustbins and embroidered cushions, she was
cast as a French starlet.

The show was planned for the week of the Kent
Sheep Dog Trials, which guaranteed an influx of
manically bored Australian sheep shearers who were in
Kent to give displays of their art to local farmers. As the
big night approached it became apparent to myself and
several others that Sue was convinced she was going to
be the first person in Kent to win a Tony. I pointed out
that there were such things as off-Broadway awards,
but this idea was ridiculous. She adopted a thick French
accent, started doing puffing exercises and constantly
inserted French words when an English one would do.
On stage she was intent on seducing the juvenile lead Dr
Sparrow, but casting had gone awry here, as he was
played by the local postmaster who was at least fifty. He
was about to playfully lift Sue up and carry her off
stage but it was apparent he wasn't up to this task. As he
bent over the sofa where Sue, in a voluminous lacy
garment obviously owned by Zsa Zsa Gabor in a past
life, lay provocatively with one foot in the air and half
her hair over one eye, he slipped a disc and fell on to the
stage literally keening in pain, before finally settling

halfway under the sofa rigidly stiff. The show ended unceremoniously with the postmaster being carried off stage on a door by six sheep shearers who kept winking at Sue.

All of this made Sue even more reticent than before. She had to rush home and light joss-sticks on all her acupuncture points. Our entire family was now addicted to the genre of amateur dramatics.

With this in mind, I joined in the discussion about the various possibilities for the entertainment evening. It came to an end when Violet said that she had heard from the dry cleaner when she picked up her sheepskin car coat that Daniel Day-Lewis had a holiday home nearby. Did anyone think he might like to open the fete in the paddock and then do a turn at the show later? It seemed to me more likely that Daniel Day-Lewis would just have a turn if he had to sit through the performance but I tactfully refrained from saying anything further.

It's very difficult to stick to one's New Year's Resolutions, I thought as the Vicar passed me a plate piled with fruit cake and steaming hot buttered scones. Every time anyone asks you over to their house you're faced with delicious homemade fare and the most mouthwatering jams made from their homegrown fruits.

One of the most difficult things for a newcomer is managing not to waste anything. When I first arrived I was truly daunted to find that Lowther left a ten-pound box of Brussels sprouts, fifteen leeks and at least twenty pounds of assorted soft fruits on the kitchen table daily. In the end, I started giving it to anyone who came to stay for the weekend as it was apparent that I was useless at bottling and preserving. It seemed even a simple chutney was beyond me.

Still savouring the Vicar's own homemade quince jelly on a crumpet, I glanced at Millicent staring at Violet who was staggering through the various stools and tables having been on a trip to see the Vicar's quilted musical toilet seat, famous because it plays the national anthem of countries as you lift up the lid, and at Christmas it plays two arias from *The Messiah* and some carols.

Unfortunately, Violet had not managed to successfully rearrange herself afterwards, and had tucked her dress into the back of a large pair of pale pink flannel passion-killers, so Millicent was tactfully steering her across the room so that the Vicar, Brian and Cedric could avert their gaze from these undergarments, the sort which haven't been seen since the Crusades.

Violet readjusted herself into a well-known phrase or saying and took a piece of Victoria sponge. Millicent and Sue were both agreeing how hard it was to watch one's waistline with such delicious food around all the time.

'It's drinking too much tea with sugar in it that gets us women fat,' noted Violet now tugging her cardigan into place. 'That's why I always put these homosexual tablets in my tea.'

Cedric, who was waving his Hermesetas at her, paused with a stricken expression on his face, and then went back to earnestly discussing the prizes for the tombola.

I reached for my fifth slice of cake and sighed ...

SUMMER

CHAPTER 5

Darling, I Forgot To Tell You
Some People Are Coming . . .

CITY DWELLERS ALWAYS THINK of a weekend in the countryside as the ultimate in unwinding. Through a rose-coloured haze they see themselves lying out on your lawn just as the weather has started to get softly warm, sipping Pimm's or Mateus Rosé out of one of those bottles with a string around it that old biddies always transform into lamp bases. As your guest lies entwined with their guest—someone from the accounts department they've always fancied for ages—they watch your children frolicking, cutting each other's fringes with the strimmer and biting slugs in half, and then they stretch languorously in the sunlight. Meanwhile, you are in the kitchen sobbing, literally turning into the human equivalent of a fat hamster on its wheel.

Picture me now, in the kitchen, the mission control of every home. I am a dull fuchsia colour and due to my husband's parsimony when it comes to domestic implements—about which he holds many of the same opinions as the Amish—I am currently cooking Sunday lunch for ten on one ring and in an oven that has two heat settings, lukewarm and blisteringly hot, neither of which I've noticed is very good for roasting potatoes so that their devious aroma wafts down the cloister like a beckoning finger. I am peeling a pile of potatoes so massive it looks exactly like the naked bottom of a clinically obese pensioner in Florida; occasionally I wipe my nose on the hem of my husband's lime green tee-shirt and look down at the serious biological stains on my track suit bottoms [four days on and counting].

It is at moments like these that you realise that the hostess of other people's country house weekends is expected to be: [1] totally unselfish and uncomplaining, never trying to sidle off to read the review section in the sunshine; [2] Marco Pierre White because you have to cook almost constantly from dawn [and if it's not cooked properly you have to pretend it's deliberately al dente]; and [3] one of those scurrying little tweenies on *Upstairs Downstairs*, hauling the sheets off the beds and changing them like a Chinese bloody launderer. Yes, there is no rest for the wicked on these weekends. You know that as you race around washing sheets, basting small animals and filling glasses, and performing a special tinkly laugh as people break all your belongings one by one.

Not that I wish to appear in any way churlish. There

are some perfect house guests and Sunday lunch guests. Invariably they are your old friends who do not expect you to look good, be witty, serve hot food on warm plates or even be there much, as they know you will be up in the primordial swamps of the baby's bathroom involved in the life-and-death struggle to get their all-in-one pyjamas on. Poor house guests always act as if you are one of the Stepford Wives, and if you don't perform perfectly they look at you as though one of your batteries has gone a bit flat.

Good guests arrive with Red Cross parcels containing violet creams and hardback books you didn't even know had been written by writers you didn't even know had been born, and then they take all your children on an SAS course, forcing them to run cross country around the nettly bit of the garden carrying a small log before encouraging them to do sixty sit-ups. When the children return red-faced and panting over the hillocks in the lawn they collapse, unconscious, into uninterrupted snores for seventeen hours, while you lie on the sofa consuming vast quantities of violet creams reading a book called *Love's Raging Torment* in total peace.

These people do exist—my friend Sue and her video magnate husband Perce are perfect guests. He was a drummer before becoming a magnate, so he is also able to make the kids drum on logs and buckets for hours, which is very tiring I've noticed. And Sue ... what can I say except that she is beautiful, tasteful and apparently this week on a special diet she got from a faith healer in Sevenoaks.

The worst kind of guests are the ones you don't

expect to come, people you don't know very well who will expect you to endure the thrust and parry of witty repartee until well after your normal bedtime of ten past eight. This will drain every fibre of your being, especially as they are always people with no children who book a vasectomy for Monday lunchtime after spending two hours in the company of my Omen 1, 2 and little 3.

It was Friday morning and Sue had driven over in her new pink wooded Morris Minor—Doris the Morris—to lie on my sofa and watch a well-known agony aunt demonstrating how to use a bidet on breakfast television. Sue and I decided that once we'd recovered from watching this tour de force of ablutions, we'd start preparing Sunday lunch two days in advance—the best way to avoid panicking, I think.

Sue, as always, was dressed truly imaginatively and extravagantly. Even at ten past nine she resembled Scarlett O'Hara in that scene where she throws the ornament at Rhett Butler and he falls on her, giving her a 'punishing kiss' as they keep calling it in *Love's Raging Torment*. Sue wore a floor-length skirt printed with bananas and ripe cherries and a ruffled red gingham blouse with a small bunch of cherries stuffed into her ample cleavage. Her tumbling curls were piled on to her head with a small basket of plastic fruits in their midst like Madame de Fontaigne. What made this ensemble even more eye-catching were the four Veganin she had Sellotaped on to her forehead, and the diet pill she had attached to each wrist.

She told me that during her last rebirthing session, which she likened to being pulled at high velocity through an orlon polo neck, the Sevenoaks psychic had informed her that she had terrible headaches all the time because she'd shot herself through the head in a past life, upset about the Wall Street Crash. The headaches were really her past life breaking through into this one like fat out of a greasy sausage. So what she'd been doing wrong was swallowing her various tablets; she should have been attaching them to her body so that they could stay in touch with her aura, her 'very troubled aura' she whispered, looking pensively out to the pear tree.

The psychic had also given her a selection of useful dieting tips which she was planning to follow this very weekend and she would definitely tell me about the results at Sunday lunch. Then the phone rang and we had to switch off the telly.

'Hello darling, it's me,' said my darling husband, still in London and about to do battle with every car on the road. 'I forgot to tell you a couple of extra people are coming down.'

'Who?' I said.

'Oh, just Tim and his new girlfriend Talisa. You know, she's the seventeen-year-old model, you know, the one everyone mistakes for someone from Mount Olympus. Not that I think she's pretty at all compared to you darling, even with that hole in your front tooth.'

LONG PAUSE.

'They'll be really easy to feed, anyway. Tim's a vegan and Talisa is on a strict macrobiotic diet so we can just give her a marrow or something.'

HIDEOUSLY LONG PAUSE.

'Well, see you later sweetie. Don't worry—I don't understand why you always insist on giving guests clean sheets anyway...'

Sue and I collapsed back on to the sofa. She is in fact originally from Chertsey, but her ancestry stretches back in an unfaltering line through Boadicea, way back to various woad-daubing peoples. At the thought of the goddess-like Talisa in our midst, another past life threatened to approach; I feared that I could shortly be sharing the sofa with the housemaid who became Pepys's mistress.

When she'd arrived in Kent she'd been mostly cross about the fact there was no Chanel boutique in Canterbury, as when Sue isn't ascending on to a higher plane, she's out shopping. She had also suspected that she'd actually had a past life in Canterbury and so she'd been rather hoping that on Saturday morning shopping trips she'd have been able to kill two birds with one stone, simultaneously reverting to some deep-seated folk memory while stocking up in Marks and Spencer on the toffee crumble ice cream with pecan nuggets and double-double chocolate chips.

I tried to cheer her up about Sunday lunch by mentioning that the goddess-like Talisa was also a vegetarian so they'd both be able to wear their MEAT IS MURDER tee-shirts, and chat about how murders occur because everyone eats too many lamb chops and fruit squash with E numbers in it. Sue rallied temporarily to say she also felt that pork luncheon meat should be made illegal and then subsided on to the sofa again, casting a malevolent gaze over me.

'God, that stupid girl's bound to be horribly vivacious as well. I bet money that she's the one—that nun that pushed me down the well in 1520.'

Hubby, Talisa and Tim were late arriving in Compton Pauncefoot. Sue had stayed to give me some moral support as the thing that we both hated most in the world, apart from unloading the drain on the washing machine and opening American Express bills, is meeting anyone new. I'd lit a huge roaring fire so that the sitting room was now about 400 degrees and I'd doused myself in Jungle Gardenia, which smells a bit like a silage plant down the road, and I was lying there trying to look like a soignée older woman. Sue had administered more Veganin and was fanning herself with a rolled-up copy of the *Country Life* peafowling edition.

As they were getting out of the car I noticed a large half-naked man in the back seat. He was wearing several large rings around his neck, a loin cloth and a pair of cloggy things. Tim explained to me that he'd taken the liberty of bringing along Nah-heed, a friend of theirs from the Amazon basin who was over for a convention about forestry techniques being held at the Post House Hotel, Heathrow. Sue took one look and said she was going to go and have a little lie down with Carlos Castaneda.

Tim and Talisa appeared to have planned to spend

most of their stay entwined in the library, Talisa lying stretching her full six-foot [three-stone] length up Tim's body, while he played with her fourteen-foot-long black hair which she was wearing in a teenage-style top knot. Not that I wish to sound at all bitter or twisted because as she was only seventeen I suppose she was allowed to wear a teenage style. What was worse was the new luv-talk argot they had adopted, which is enough to make even a staunch consumer of *Love's Raging Torment* ill.

'Oh, Twinky, I do luvey wuvey you,' gasped Talisa, having now rolled into a prone position on the Persian carpet, with Tim flat on top of her.

'And I wuveys youzees touzees,' replied Tim, with an admirably straight face, reaching down to pull his jeans out of his bottom and swat a fly. Husband places the *Independent*, *Spectator* and *The Life of Pepys* on his face all at the same time, something I'd always thought he was saving for a nuclear attack.

By the evening I was exhausted. I longed to go to bed as early as possible. I washed the girls in the bath; the sun was streaming through the stained-glass roses in the window, making patterns in the bubbly water, which looked like pink ice cream. They were delighting in the hot weather especially as we had filled our illegal paddling pool that afternoon.

In their bedroom, I admired Honey's soft shining hair, praised Harmony's brown damp skin like that of a beautiful porpoise, and marvelled at Heavenly's legs. In her shortie nightie they resembled two twiglets.

They slowly fell asleep, all cuddling each other, their damp hair making little patterns on the pillow. Honey snored gently through her open mouth, Harmony mumbled in her sleep and Heavenly cuddled her baby doll close.

I looked out of the window, happy not to be downstairs making Pimm's. In the luscious half-light at the end of a summer's day, with the long shadows of the tower playing across the front lawn and the smell of roses wafting around the children's window, I leaned out slightly and picked a bloom. I put it next to Honey's little pink face because it would delight her when she woke up.

Getting ready for bed early, unable to stand any more undercurrents of romance eddying around the sofa, I noticed that since Talisa had been in the house I appeared to have shrunk six inches and put on three stone. Interesting, I thought, falling asleep as I hit the pillow...

The next morning Talisa looked at me, in her own special unblinking way. 'I don't want to be any trouble you know,' she said. 'I'll eat anything as long as it's an organic pulse.'

'Oh, sweetums, youzee's so helpful to Mumsy Wumsy,' said Tim. I felt deeply wounded at the term Mumsy Wumsy and left, trailed by kids.

Some minutes later Talisa came into the kitchen with the tray, which teetered with various other mouldy teacups she'd discovered lurking under all the chairs. 'I won't wash up,' she announced, 'because I don't know where anything goes, so it might make more work for you.' With that, she dumped the tray and went back to Tim.

The children were fascinated by the constantly entwined limbs of Tim and Talisa. They stood in a row in front of them like three monkeys, staring.

'Are you sexing with her?' said Harmony. 'If you are can I watch because Mum and Dad won't let me and I'm still not sure what happens.'

'No,' said Tim shortly, wiping a little piece of sick off the leg of his Levi's.

'We're always talking about sexing at school now,' said Harmony.

'It's called making love, not sexing,' said Tim tersely. Talisa giggled and ran her fingers through his hair, and I mean hair singular.

'Mum says Talisa is a slapper,' said Harmony. 'What's a slapper, Dad?'

Before he could answer, Honey, who had been frolicking as naked as a summer spirit in the garden, entered through the french windows. As she kneeled down to pick up something glittering from next to Tim's head, she had a little accident.

'Tim,' said Harmony. 'Honey has weed on the back of your head. Does it feel really funny when that happens and you're sexing?'

Because of this myriad of organisational problems inherent to keeping everyone happy all of the time, I'd actually completely forgotten at this point about Nahheed and his furry loin cloth. It wasn't until my spouse wandered in wild-eyed that I realised that something was afoot. It transpired that he had found Nah-heed in the garden next door ripping up small shrubs and rose bushes, and had had to persuade him back to rip up ours instead. Apparently he was going to build a sweat-lodge in the garden so that everyone could get into it semi-naked and pray to the tree god Patootle.

'I'm not doing that,' said Sue resolutely. 'I refused to mime *Swedish Blow-Job* and Big Country in charades last Christmas and I am *not* getting half-naked into a geodesic dome made out of four rosebushes with him and that model, no matter how personally meaningful the experience could be.'

'I'm not doing it either,' I added. 'I'll order a Chinese takeaway for you all.'

So the last we saw of the dynamic foursome was Perce's wine red bri-nylon paisley-patterned Y-fronts vanishing into the tunnel entrance of Nah-heed's sweat-lodge. We heard a lot of chanting, which turned to terrible coughing as the camp fire inside got smokier, and the bodies of Nah-heed, Tim, Talisa and Perce got sweatier.

'I hope Perce doesn't get one of his attacks,' commented Sue, sagely strapping a Veganin to her cleavage.

The rest of the weekend went in a whirlwind of laundry, kids, making meals for ninety, tea for ninety and changing Nah-heed's sheets because the monosodium glutamate had disagreed with him rather badly. Next morning I was back in my lemon quilted housecoat, not really caring if Talisa emerged in a gold Lycra catsuit with tassels attached.

She walked into breakfast looking sunkissed, but that could have been the burns from the sweat-lodge the night before. She took a piece of toast, then demonstrated a talent hitherto only displayed by Daniel Day-Lewis in *The Bounty*—the ability to chew and suck one's cheeks in at the same time.

'Gosh, Tim just told me that you had your birthday the same day as mine,' she said.

'Hmmm,' I replied, lurching towards the kettle.

'Isn't that a coincidence?' she chortled. 'Gosh, I was seventeen and you were thirty on the same day. Golly, that is funny, isn't it, Mumsy Wumsy?'

'Staying with you has been like a huge contraceptive really,' said Tim charmingly as they got into their car to leave. Nah-heed stamped his foot and hit me on either side of the temple with a piece of bark he'd collected and got into the back.

Talisa said, 'Thank youee woozee for having little meezee weezee,' and off they went, leaving Sue and me on the sofa with a big plate of cakes between us.

'I just know she pushed me down that well you know,' said Sue, halving a Battenburg cake and handing me one half ...

CHAPTER 6

The Crime Wave

FOR THE SECOND DAY RUNNING the sun had scorched the damp fields and hedgerows. It soaked into the crumbling rust-coloured brick walls surrounding the orchards and bounced from the reflective grey slates of the curiously shaped church tower, blinding everyone who looked up from their allotment to wipe the sweat from their brow.

A drought was immediately declared. It was nice to see this tradition maintained—all the hallmarks of approaching English summer immediately became apparent. It was reassuring to see the outbreak of tabloid headlines carried after any eight-hour period of consecutive sunshine. Unanimously they screamed PHEW! or IT'S COSTA DEL KENT! and showed pictures of a crimson handkerchief-headed pot-bellied gent, his

93

sleeves and cuffs rolled up, his waistband loose and the cleavage of his buttocks rising coquettishly like a bizarre travesty of St Tropez above the elastic of his Union Jack underwear

It was summer. It had rained its way through February and blown us all up into the air through March and April but come June the farmers and the travel agents thanked God. Gardeners panicked, but Lowther, being easy in the ways of Kent, his garden and the weather, had primed his oak barrels for the inevitable and now they overflowed with water. Sub-barrels and smaller buckets picked up every drop. The casual passer-by would have looked at these precautions and glanced up at the bucketing skies, smiling to himself before moving on. But Lowther knew. It was the same every year and he was nothing if not a traditionalist. Within twenty-eight hours of the first glimpse of a pallid English sun, the Kent hosepipe ban was in effect once again.

I decided I'd better go and tell Dorcas.

'Hiough, have MERCY,' Dorcas shouted loudly from the kitchenette over the *splot splot splot* of tomato ketchup on a large full English breakfast she'd made to keep her strength up during the hot spell. She shimmied very quickly through the bead curtain in a floral shortie nightie and slippers shaped like the Duke of Edinburgh.

'YEAH BAY-BEEEEEE,' she warbled along to 'Fifties Motown Hits' in a frighteningly loud falsetto. Her telephone was ringing and the little gas log fire burned merrily in the grate. She handed me my tea in a large mug that read THINNER THIGHS IN THIRTY DAYS on the front. Half of it sloshed over my bare leg, and the rest slopped on to the chintz covers when Dorcas threw herself on to the end of the couch with her laden plate.

She went back into the kitchen for more ketchup, and then emerged a few moments later singing 'I heard it through the grapevine' into a half frozen chipolata.

'GORRD,' she exclaimed. 'This hot weather makes me feel like a vixen.'

She lay down next to me to discuss our favourite subject, the hot weather. Her nightie rode up to reveal a large pair of rather loathsome crêpe-de-chine cami-knickers. She was panting gently, and a small patch of sweat was forming across her large bosom.

'Oh the he-yat, the he-yat,' she said in a perfect Southern belle's accent, fanning herself and asking me if I'd mind switching the gas log fire off as the room had the same heady atmosphere as a Club 18–30 holiday in Tierra del Fuego. I obliged immediately.

'I like to have the fire on all the time,' she told me. 'It makes me feel sexy.'

Dorcas told me that she thought she was in love again. Everyone around here decorates their homes with hop vines; like corn dollies, these are an integral part of interior decorating in Kent. Out 'shopping' at the local hop farm, Dorcas had seen a completely gorgeous boy working there, so she'd ordered loads of dried hops to drape round the bed because the farm had a delivery service, so she was hoping that they'd send him along to deliver it. 'He was totally beautiful, you know. The only trouble was that he did look suspiciously young, like he might still be doing his mock O-Levels or whatever it is they do now. And the other thing that was wrong was he had one of those really thick Kentish accents. When he was saying hello I kept thinking that he sounded like Keanu Reeves in an Ealing comedy.'

I went into the kitchen and got another Coca-Cola. When I came back Dorcas was standing with her head stuck out of the window, her bosom resting on the window-box, crushing the wall flowers. She rubbed her cold can across her cleavage and sighed. 'I hope the weather stays like this. If this is global warming, I'm totally in favour of it.'

I was glad to see her back on form after her horrible embarrassment with Daniel Day-Lewis. 'Oh, that,' she said airily. 'I never think of him now, although knowing my luck the reason he took so long to bring my dress back was because he was wearing it at home.' I said I didn't think it would fit him.

'Anyway, I prefer this boy at the hop farm.' The phone rang and Dorcas let it ring twice so she wouldn't look too keen. It was the hop farm saying her boxes would be over at twelve.

I went home to see that everything was all right, and was amazed at how blisteringly hot it was for so early in the day. The sky was a perfect delphinium blue, the borders had burst into flower all at once and even

Lowther, who was so worried about the hosepipe ban, could walk around with a blissful expression on his face, as this was the moment when all his back-breaking toil became apparent.

The grass was a carpet of tiny daisies and flat saucer dandelions, and clouds of meadow-sweet made a haze in the distance. Birds sang contralto and under the eaves the starlings' nests were packed with new babies all simultaneously making unpleasant greedy regurgitations down the side of the newly painted house.

It's also so easy to get out of bed in the summer. The sight of the garden unfolding beneath you and the promise of hours to be spent outside doing nothing more energetic than picking a lilac bloom and eating jelly is enticing. And despite the constant warnings of dermatologists I still religiously try to tan my skin like an old saddle, lying prone in the beating sun.

When I first wake up now I not only fling open the windows but also make sure I pull across the vast heavy bolts on the old door which leads out on to the balcony outside our bedroom. It is an enormous space, but sadly has no railing around it [other than a wisteria of great age]. This means that it is out of bounds to the children who would immediately plummet kamikaze fashion off the edge—my children can't stand on an upturned bucket without breaking a limb so they definitely can't go out on the balcony. The other problem is the lead roof which retains heat so that each morning, when I go out there to trill at nature as it trills back at me, I scald my feet and leap from one foot to the other, clutching at the gnarled old branches of wisteria for support, shouting down to the children not to lean their bikes on the dog.

Every summer's day has its rituals—visiting Dorcas to hear about her love life and to discuss the weather, flinging open every single door in the house, propping them open all day long with pots full of plants so that cool breezes can circulate, bringing with them the pollen, scents and leaves of a million roses. I could tell this was going to be another perfect summer's day to savour. It would be light until late which meant the children would be able to just stay up until they fell asleep, which is another advantage of summer. If you did that in winter it would just mean trying to concentrate on Inspector Morse while three small people argued ferociously and continuously about who held the cat next.

It would be so nice for English children if we had a wonderful climate and they could spend all day naked, never having to put on horrible prickly underwear that was surgically attached to their vests and then topped off with a snow suit. I hope all they remember is the summer—building dens out of blankets and eating too many strawberries.

Honey was in the kitchen, sitting at the table drawing. Lying next to her on the table was a small roll of pink toilet paper which she occasionally broke off from her drawing to croon at, and pat. I made some tea, and then looked closer at her bundle of loo roll, only to see it was a huge slug swaddled up in a truss. 'No one wanted to be my best friend except him,' she told me dramatically, kissing the top of its head tenderly.

I had promised Dorcas I'd go back later on and see

what had happened with Prince Charming. At about ten past twelve I left everyone happily splashing in the illegal paddling pool and went across the road to see Dorcas's new paramour. He was already there looking rather dazed.

'I've never done a home delivery before,' he told me. 'When she answered the door in them big ol' nick-nacks I got a bit of a shock.'

Dorcas nodded smugly. 'He did,' she assured me, delighted. He was extraordinarily handsome; his trousers hung hopelessly off his thin hips, and he didn't have to try very hard. He just stood there with his big blue eyes and his shirt hanging out. I almost felt sorry for him when he accepted Dorcas's invitation to come over and watch *Blue Peter* next week.

'That was a nifty move,' she said when he'd gone again. 'I asked him over for that because I suddenly had this horrible feeling he might be fourteen or something ghastly like that. I'm so hot I might come over to your place and get in that little plastic pool of yours.' She picked a bit of dust off her shoulder and wiped a small bead of sweat off the side of her face. 'Actually, I love *Blue Peter*, although I don't think it's ever been the same since Peter Purves left.'

I agreed.

'Do you think he had a big one?' she called as I wandered home, clutching a magazine she'd lent me. Two headlines had caught my notice: 'Aliens Steal Elvis's Prostate' and 'Routine Wart Operation Goes Tragically Wrong: Man Blows Up On Operating Table'. Not for Dorcas the local paper and *Country Life*.

New Yorkers always say that the minute the weather gets hot, sultry and rather wonderful, it triggers something other than an incredible feeling of well-being, good temper and a desire to rip off one's clothes. They would tell us it also triggers criminal tendencies. And in the last few weeks it is true that we have been experiencing our first real crime wave. Previously we were a community where hardly anyone locked their doors, and where it was still safe to leave the key under a plant pot, even though everyone knows that was where you had left it. But now things have changed rapidly, although it hasn't reached the point of our nights being interrupted by the constant wailing of the police sirens.

Ours is a community that is a testament to the joys of a local bobby who plods around and gets to know everyone as soon as they are born, which gives him the right to clip naughty boys around the ear when they are caught defacing public toilets and writing their names on the side of the bus shelter, often nipping in the bud any further activities without any trips to juvenile court. Tom is about thirty-eight and round, wearing his helmet proudly all the time, along with very thick glasses. One can't help but notice how unflattering a police helmet is to anyone with several chins and a very red face, but he is a keen crime fighter so his lack of a sartorial splendour is ignored. He travels everywhere on his bike, clips in place, his jacket flapping slightly around his rounded bottom which he always sticks right in the air as he steers his way up our steep hill, and his tie frequently stuck sideways where he has tried to loosen his collar and then forgotten about it.

Last week he had one of the biggest coups of his career when he arrested the Vicar. The Vicar was actually caught red-handed using his hosepipe on his ornamental wheelbarrow full of zinnias during the ban. He tried to do this under cover of darkness, but Tom heard the trickly noise of his leaking hosepipe [a lesson to us all]. This resulted in a stiff fifty-pound fine, a stiff letter from the Archbishop saying that he hoped this was the last time he'd be seen in court except on jury duty, and, worst of all, a horribly unflattering picture of him, with his eyes half shut and a candlewick cap on his head, appeared on the front of the *Bugle*. As Lowther said, it was a picture that made him look like a real fugitive from the law.

Tom, however, was delighted to have made an arrest, and such a splash with it too. It seemed that his little legs were throbbing around the town even faster since and that he was even more vigilantly trying to catch anyone daring to water their runner beans. And as the weather got hotter and hotter day by day, men like Lowther began to look like the sort of desperadoes who would use the water out of the paddling pool if necessary.

But, as if in retribution for their asking for water, the crime wave was to affect keen horticulturists most of all. A gang, popularly thought to come from one of the council estates in a nearby town, started to break into garden sheds, stealing lawn mowers, strimmers, hedge clippers and anything else that could be easily put into the back of a van. In one garden they obviously got a little carried away as they attempted to make off with the septic tank, which weighed a ton. Instead of getting hernias they left it on the pavement outside.

Tom must have started to feel like he was in the Tour de France, shooting around town, his feet pounding along the pavements before he leaped on to his bike to race off to write another detailed description of a pair of secateurs. Either feast or famine, because up until now the only complaints had come in the form of three phone calls, from the owner of the Pekinese who was in heat at the bottom of our hill who found her house entirely surrounded by local dogs looking hopeful, from a woman who'd rung to insist that an arrest was made because her neighbour's bonfire had scorched three liberty bodices, and from the owner of Earl Spencer's Slug Pellet about the Vicar's cleaner's ex-husband urinating against the door to the snug and causing a disturbance.

Millicent was convinced that the Vicar was Mr Big. Lowther naturally agreed with that immediately and Dorcas claimed it was only a matter of time before the gang turned to the white slave trade and tried to steal beautiful women off the streets.

In fact, it wasn't the white slave trade that they turned to next; it was something much worse. During the night the front doors of St Perbold's were kicked in and the only thing of value that the church possessed, a beautiful silver and red glass chalice dating back to mediaeval times and only used on high days of great importance, was stolen. We lived on top of the church, but we hadn't heard a thing. Despite the fact the doors had been kicked open we had slept through the whole crime.

Even stranger things were to come. Next morning Growler had vanished as well. This caused the children great consternation as they were convinced that he was taken for a ransom. They sat by the phone waiting for instructions about where to leave the fourteen pence they had gathered together from down the back of the sofa. We went out and searched the garden for the dog.

Then we went out into the street calling his name, but he was nowhere to be found. It was most odd, as he never usually goes anywhere. Even I felt a little shaky and found myself making those familiar deal-type prayers, offering never to hit him with the toilet brush again if he could turn up safely.

At lunchtime the CID arrived in a shiny car, which made me realise things were getting serious and perhaps organised crime had moved into Sittingbourne. After speaking to them, I was even more surprised that I'd heard nothing, as apparently the thieves had not only broken open the front door, but also knocked over several pews trying to get to the votive candles to light their cigarettes, which struck me as rather a leisurely way to burgle. As the two policemen sat at the kitchen table making copious notes in their books, Dorcas arrived and had to sit through fifteen minutes of rather tedious discussion about everyone's exact whereabouts during the night.

Finally, they snapped their notebooks shut, smartly saluted and left us with our tea cups. Dorcas turned to me immediately. 'I'd have married either of them,' she told me, 'but I think I preferred the one with the blue pencil. Did you notice the other one had a massive pustule on his neck—I'd be worried about it bursting while we were together.'

I rang the police later to see if there had been any sightings of the stupid dog. By now I could have strangled him with my bare hands, but no one had seen him. I hoped that he hadn't seen the thieves and been kicked or harmed, but comforted myself with the thought that the smell of him alone would put them off getting too close.

Anyone who has lost a dog will tell you how the hours stretch on as if you're in a black hole or a vortex. As soon as my husband came home the recriminations started in earnest; apparently the dog would never have felt the need to leave home if I hadn't chastised him constantly for having a weak anal sphincter. The children glared accusingly at me across their pasties. Recriminations went on for most of the evening.

By bedtime, as three hurt faces looked at me, I felt as if we were reenacting the kidnapping of the Lindbergh baby rather than a stupid twit of a dog that had temporarily absconded to eat rubbish out of bins further afield. I went downstairs having tucked the three angels into their bed. Husband was—bizarrely—wearing a tartan smoking jacket, standing with one foot on the club fender and one arm along the mantelpiece, looking at a snapshot of the dog. 'You've never liked him, at least you could admit that,' he said mistily.

Realise that Husband is the type that will probably blame me for not having let the plug out of the bath three days ago if floods occur in Bangladesh, and know that secretly he blames me for the depletion of the water table because I was once caught having a deep bath. Realise that married life is a hard struggle at times, and have a brief vision of myself as a single chick, riding a purple Vespa up the Spanish Steps in a pair of lilac Capri pants with a lot of wolf whistles echoing around me. Sadly realise I am not a girl who spends her spare time rising out of birthday cakes like Venus, wearing bikinis made of whipped cream, but more the type who takes a bath in two inches of lukewarm water and a dash of Dettol to kill off any sheepticks I've picked up in the fields.

I was woken up at ten past six on Saturday morning by Tom, saying that Growler was now in police custody.

The afternoon before he'd been found running around the cricket fields having become furiously over-excited at the close proximity of some new and interesting rubbish bags he hadn't ripped open before. But it was almost impossible to catch him and a scene worthy of a silent comedy film had ensued with Tom, his legs racing like pistons, and the sergeant with the terrible pustule on the side of the neck racing around in great circles while Growler yapped and farted furiously, thrilled at this unexpected game. He then exited the field between Tom's legs and hared off towards the boys' toilets behind the Pony Club tents. Finally, he was lured into their trap by Tom waving a large double scoop 99 cornet at him.

'Don't seem to like the cornet bit much, which surprised me,' said Tom on the phone. ''Cos we'd already had two sightings of him that morning eating the polystyrene packages off containers outside the Wimpy.'

I said that he'd always been willing to eat almost anything but maybe the unusual exercises had tired him out so he couldn't manage the cornet.

'Got a lot of troubles in 'is innards, ain't he?' he noted tersely, ''e 'ad a terrible accident in the back of the panda car on the way to the station. Bloody frightful it was.'

He took me down to Growler's lonely cell where he was sitting on the bare bed musing to himself in a shaft of watery sunlight which filtered through the high narrow window overhead, giving him a look of a small hairy short-legged Bunyan.

I gave him a swift kick up the bottom for his trouble and stuffed him into the back of the car where he sat looking out of the window, surly at the lack of a huge welcome—which he got when we arrived home anyway. Not that he deserved it, I thought crossly. Irritating little bugger.

But the thefts continued unabated until it was decided something obvious had to be done to track down the culprits. Two young local men who lived on the other side of the cricket field quite near to Millicent and Brian's homes were now suspected. Obviously they hadn't realised that the strong arms of the law were moving ever closer around them, as the thefts had now increased so that almost nightly raids were being made on sheds and gardens. We had already lost our three-seater garden seat, and they had also kicked in the door to the coal shed, obviously thinking Lowther kept further implements in there. When would it end?

Dorcas rang me to remind me that tonight was the night for her big date—did I want to come over and help her get the place ready for Loveday?

'Loveday?' I gasped.

'Loveday,' she replied firmly, in a voice that would brook no further discussion. 'And I think it's a bit much coming from you to say anything about funny names,' she retorted, sniffing. In truth, Loveday was shy and pathetic and rural, so Dorcas didn't want him to be alone with her. I was to play the chaperone.

When I arrived, Dorcas, a woman who believes that playing hard to get means making men wait until she's finished her pudding, had been in turmoil. She had a feeling that Loveday might get scared witless if there were too much of a romantic ambience. I pointed out that at ten past five in the afternoon there isn't a lot of scope for a sexy atmosphere but she fixed me with such a withering look that I gave up and helped her put 150-watt bulbs in all the lamps. In a way she was right. Loveday was not only young, but he was also a local boy, which meant he was terrified of being in a room with less than thirty people after four in the afternoon.

Dorcas had got *Labyrinth* out on video for them, which, as this is a film for thirteen-year-olds, showed what she thought of Loveday. She had estimated he had the IQ of a begonia. In the end we all sat on the sofa in a row and I had to keep explaining the plot because he said it was too complicated.

Just as Dorcas was mouthing 'Go away' at me and making semaphore signals over his head while he drank his fourth can of beer, he toppled over sideways and fell asleep.

'Crikey,' said Dorcas. 'He's got bloody narcolepsy.' She gave him a kiss on the cheek as he lay there. 'I mean, if we're talking safe sex, you can't get much safer than this, someone who's actually unconscious, can you?'

I helped her to heave him upstairs, where in her spare room he managed to take his trousers off, looking worryingly like a small boy who's just learned to remove his clothes without falling over. I wondered aloud if he was on drugs when he bought his boxer shorts.

Dorcas told me I knew nothing of men's fashion and that it was very fashionable to have Kylie Minogue's face on your underpants.

'He looks a bit like Bambi, doesn't he?' she said peering closely at him. 'He's got quite a lot of hair on his chest for someone very young, hasn't he? At least that shows he's reached puberty, which is a relief.'

Dorcas started chortling at her own joke as usual, and fell over the step out of the bedroom.

'Anyway,' she said comforting herself, 'lots of people look young when they're comatose.'

Our good weather continued for the next couple of weeks so I started to make a habit of going out on to the balcony at night as well, so that I could savour those last moments of the day. The blue skies, filled with puffy little clouds painted on by Edward Ardizzone during the day, gave way to huge black skies, great Steven Spielberg vistas of stars and swirling clouds that had crumbled up into little dots of twinkling lights above us. In London it's impossible ever to see this breathtaking sight, as the light pollution of a million traffic lights and a thousand neon signs advertising tandoori chicken balls drowns out the delicate patches above. But here there is a show nightly, and I started to encourage the girls to think about a night under the stars on a mattress in the garden, but Honey insisted the damp would destroy her hair, Heavenly couldn't spend any time away from my chest and Harmony was worried that an animal would eat her.

'What animal?' I said rather crossly at this lack of enthusiasm. What kind of children am I raising? How will they fare on an outward bound course, when one of them has to be breastfed every ten minutes, another has to have a beauty case with her that's so heavy it requires seventeen Sherpas to lift it and the eldest would rather spend all her time on a horse with a Game Boy and a family-size Yorkie Bar?

The local council published the results of their extensive research into the duck pond which proved that all the ducks are at least three hundred per cent overweight. This is because they are constantly fed large loaves of white bread by all the neighbourhood children. The only person who was probably really interested in the findings was the fox who lives in our garden and now has three young. He can often be seen with his mate, ferrying the little ones for no apparent reason back and forth across the paddock, although I suspect it is to keep the sheep on their toes with a quick thrust of adrenaline every couple of days.

The other evening I was in the cloister garden when he came up behind me and, astonishingly tame, gently touched the back of my leg with a fine nose. Although this sounds wonderful, I was at first terrified because of the unexpectedness of it, but then rushed into the kitchen to fill a bowl with stew which he eagerly ate up. Not that he has any need for my scraps, living as he does on duck à l'orange all week long with the luxurious nightly diet of chubby mallards and rotund moorhens. One of the things that understandably put Harmony off sleeping in the garden was the constant sounds of duck bones being crunched in the undergrowth.

CHAPTER 7

Sue And I Join
The Women's Institute

SUMMER CONTINUED WITH A GLORIOUS SPLASH of
colourful flowers and dry sultry heat, but Lowther became more and more morose, praying daily
for rain. He was also very depressed about the
assaults birds were making on the fig tree, and
had draped the whole area in the bunting left over from
the fete last year—occasionally he could be seen running
out of his house brandishing two maracas in the
direction of braver birds pecking at the luscious fruits
ripening in the sunlight.

Despite his depression, Millicent and Sue [among
others] suspected that Lowther was in fact watering the
plants on the quiet. I doubted this else why would he
have gone to such trouble rigging up all the Heath
Robinson-like devices we now had at the bottom of all

our pipes, catching all the bath water and sink water when it came gushing out? In the name of conservation, he could also be found on his hands and knees every morning, dabbing at the leaves of his favourite plants with lotions and unguents designed to make them less hot. We were the only people in the area whose camellias were wearing stronger sunblock than we were.

The drought was now mentioned on the radio and TV all the time. Even the front page of the *Evening Bugle* was devoted to the debate on the council about whether the hosepipe ban should extend to the municipal bedding plants outside the police station, or whether they should be granted a dispensation as there was to be a civic visit from the Duchess of Gloucester in two weeks' time.

I felt as if I was in one of those BBC plays set in a drought-stricken 2004, especially as in those things the entire cast is always clad in what appears to be my Emerson Fittipaldi boiler suit. More worrying still, they always drive around in cars that resemble the steel tubes around cigars and have four-course meals in tablet form, all of which might happen here if this hot weather continues.

Something new had happened though—we had new neighbours. Ralph and Debbie were both hard at work at the bottom of the hill like latterday Mad King Ludwigs, transforming the simple clapboard cottage they had bought into some alpine ski chalet, with a couple of minarets thrown in for good measure. Every time I walked past, the sounds of frenzied sanding, grinding and rusticating could be heard. So far, Ralph had painstakingly added lead strips to all his double glazing and now he was stripping pine like it was auditioning for the Raymond Revue Bar.

I felt Ralph was turning out to be an interesting dichotomy, a communist with a country cottage who was also a member of the Rotary Club, but that was before I realised that he and Debbie would join almost anything given the encouragement.

Millicent had met them both several times at the Mayor's weekly wine and cheese evenings, when he invites the comrades round to drink advocaat, throw darts at a yellowing poster of Mrs Thatcher and write long letters to *Marxism Today*. Dorcas had also met them and thought that Ralph was really sexy because he looked like one of those upper-class actors who always play repressed men in wing collars.

In order to be welcoming, I invited him and Debbie around for tea, but he annoyed me by continually putting his hands together in front of his face like a little steeple, before sighing gustily and asking why we needed so much space for one family. Then he asked me if I'd ever read Paul Foot's *Red Shelley*.

'I saw you washing your car the other day with a long yellow hosepipe,' I told him by way of a feisty riposte. 'Do you know about the hosepipe ban?' I flung at him. 'On hosepipes?'

He looked baffled and for some reason thought I'd said 'on headlights'.

'I love a woman who's existential,' he told me.

'It's been terribly hard finding a Gothic manhole cover,' added Debbie brightly, obviously wanting to seem alluring.

'Doesn't matter I'm still happy,' he added. 'Really bucked the system today actually. As you may have heard I've been the secretary of the local Rotary Club for the past year, in sole charge of the annual dinner dance and cabaret. Brilliant fun it's been, so I was gutted—gutted—when I found out that you have to retire when you're forty! Couldn't believe it after I'd managed to get Buck's Fizz to perform for the dinner last year and all. So today I dropped my passport down the loo, rubbed around the date of birth a bit and— Bob's your uncle!'

'Or your husband,' snorted Debbie, gaily chortling.

We parted amicably and I promised to go down and see the work in progress at their house later that day.

Sue rang me later that afternoon to say that she was entering the fourth dimension. She'd filled her bath with Epsom Salts and had leapt in hoping it would have the same effect as an isolation tank, but she had a lot of little scratches from pruning the creepers back last week, so they stung like fury and she'd had to get out again.

'But then I decided I'd just sit on the sofa and listen to my new tape of Carl Sagan reading selected passages of *Jonathan Livingstone Seagull* so I could feel myself floating away from worldly possessions.'

I put the phone down, made sure the children were still alive and painting, and ambled down the hill to see what the new neighbours had done to the house in the last ten minutes. Debbie answered the door wearing a 1940s dress and flip-flops. Inside, Ralph had one of the comrades over and they were both listening to some seminal Goth death music circa 1978, and rereading passages from the *Thief's Journal* to one another. Personally, I felt this was not the sort of thing anyone should be doing in a small market town anywhere. Instead I asked to see upstairs.

One of the awful things for people who arrive from London and think they can settle in to their country cottage immediately is that it means six months of living on a building site while they turn it into their own urban vision of a rustic dreamhome. I was reminded of this as the upstairs bedroom swung open to reveal three double-glazing salesmen, the plasterer and the man from the council who'd come to check the depth of their manhole sitting in a semi-circle, like a coven, around a copy of the *Sun* and a pot of tea.

Hastily standing up and adjusting themselves, they greeted us and tried to pretend that the three-day-old copy of the *Sun* was a blueprint that required intensive scrutiny, and not a Page Three photo of two trainee hairdressers from Neasden posing in living colour with a glockenspiel. We retreated downstairs.

'The kitchen is almost finished,' said Debbie brightly, 'and Ralph says there might even be room for an Aga if we don't try and open the back door again.'

As we looked mutely at the back door wondering whether it'd be annoying to have to climb out of the larder window every time she wanted to sit in the garden, or if it was worth it for an Aga, she told me she'd now joined the fete committee.

'I'm fighting with every fibre of my being the idea of an entertainment evening,' she said. 'I went to one in Ospringe the other night and suddenly the doctor, who'd examined my piles at the health centre last week, leaped up on stage and performed 'Hot Voodoo' in a red beaded dress and a feathery bolero. I didn't know where to look and I said to Ralph that this was the sort of humiliation one had to expect if you had entertainments in a small community.'

We took our tea into the other room. The comrade had taken off his donkey jacket to reveal he was wearing nothing underneath but his entire torso was covered with a tattoo of barbed wire, and he had Lenin on his shoulder blade. He told me that he'd just returned from a weekend visit to Moscow with some members of the Militant Vegetarian Left-Wing Rotary Club. Despite his affiliation with all things Russian, he said, 'I still felt nervous when they told me that even now sixty per cent of all Russian hotel rooms are bugged. I found myself, literally as soon as I'd put my rucksack down on the floor, making impassioned pro-Russian speeches into the bedside lampshade, and I did another one straight into the shower attachment for good measure.' Still he said it made him happy to see his comrades and he'd got a huge tin of caviar for only four quid.

I said goodbye because Debbie had to race off to a match with the ladies' netball team and Ralph was off to an apple juice sampling party held by the local Orchard Union. When I got home I thought I should definitely join something. I've noticed that three things happened to me when I moved out of town. Firstly, my wardrobe changed drastically. I realised that lots of farmers sport old trousers and wellington boots with the sort of moth-eaten duffel coats that would even get thrown off a CND rally and, as I was desperate to blend in with the locals, I attempted to don identical apparel [especially as I had noticed how hard it is to get over a stile in an Anthony Price hobble skirt and four-inch purple sparkly stilettoes]. Secondly, I lost a lot of my svelte power-dressed urban girlfriends, but that was partly because they were fed up of trying to have interesting discussions with me about Guatemalan politics while someone under three feet tall hit them rhythmically on the side of the head with a Tonka truck. The final and most earth-shattering thing that happened to me is that I joined the Women's Institute.

Sue also longed to be a member of that most revered, longlasting and delightful of all our English institutions. Having said that, I think that one of the main reasons she wanted to join was so that she could have first dibs on all the Victoria sponges. She also thought that it would help her to become more proficient at flower arranging, and to create something more inspired than her usual vast bunches flung into vases, or her Japanese-themed arrangements which always seemed to consist of two twigs and some purple scabious in a ten-year-old bit of oasis. I just wanted to get my hands on loads of those hand-knitted gnome families they always make, even if it did mean sitting through three-hour slide shows about the botany of Corfu in a very chilly town hall.

My granny was a member of the North Wales branch of the WI and at the age of eighty-five discovered that she had a hidden talent for watercolours and spent years painting a small cliff near Llandudno called the Little Orme before moving on to her next muse, the Great Orme. She even contributed paintings to the WI Art Society and was photographed for the *North Wales Weekly News* clad in a jauntily tipped beret with a paint-splattered smock clutching five tubes of yellow ochre paint in an arthritic hand.

I had always felt that the WI seemed a bit like the masons, or even the Rotary Club, rather mysterious and grown-up. If someone had told Sue and me that there was a secret apron wiggle for members we would have believed them. I also half expected not to get in; my sponges often look like they're suffering from a San Andreas fault and I have no idea how to knit Mrs Santa Claus or the Three Bears in lime green wool remnants. In fact, wool is one of the great mysteries of the Women's Institute—all of my children have spent at least their first six months clad in tiny jumpers and cardigans acquired at bazaars, and invariably they are lime green, powder blue and neon pink combined with a heathery wool trim.

Despite these worries, I was very excited on Tuesday as I drove over to meet Sue and we set off together to join

up. The big day, I suspected, would only be marred by
Sue's choice of outfit for her inaugural visit. I knew she
was not going to blend in like myself.

As I walked into the drawing room the smell of
magnolia blossoms, huge droopy hothouse lilies and
exotic flowers in glorious bowls hit me; it mingled with
incense and two bowls of Chappie Sue had put out for
Growler and her own dog to eat. She moved a small
mountain of frilly tapestry cushions to one side; I
noticed one still had the auction tag on it, and another
had a small price tag saying £460 so I studiously
avoided leaning on them. We sat with a large plate of
Mr Kipling's Battenburg fancies between us, watching
the Jane Fonda advanced workout flickering silently on
TV, though occasionally Sue flicked over to watch two
ladies from Slough earnestly discussing colonic irrigation with Kilroy.

Sue had already done the I Ching four times to decide
what to wear, so she was unsuitably resplendent in a
hooped organza ballgownish affair covered in sequin
Wisteria, dark curls tumbling down her back. A small
branch of fake apple blossom held her fringe aloft, and
perched atop the whole teetering edifice was a small
stuffed bird. A tit willow, she told me.

I casually mentioned that tradition decreed that one
should wear a tweedy A-line skirt with a delicious
lemony-coloured twin set. I had visualised myself as a
heady communion between Celia Johnson and one of
those Agatha Christie heroines who murders the parlour
maid with their husband's best niblick. Sue remained
unconvinced but said she couldn't recall Christian

Lacroix doing anything A-line recently. I comforted myself thinking that if the WI ever held a fete her calling was obvious—Sue would be stuffed into a tent and told to read fortunes for the day.

She was just going into the kitchen to get a few crumpets out of her hand-painted tartan breadbin, when the glorious ambience of delicious scents and decorations was shattered by the most appalling smell imaginable. It was the sort of smell that Russian spies waft down phone receivers in Cold War movies so that the hero immediately collapses on to the floor revealing everything and clutching his nose screaming. I looked around to see with horror that Growler's Chappie had rushed straight through him, probably because of the tin of Cookin sauce he'd consumed earlier that day. He'd not only left a hideous deposit on her Aubusson rug, but also leaped on to the solid gold cushion with the price tag on the sofa and wiped his bum on it.

Sue was immediately on the verge of departing to a past life. It was going to be just my luck to arrive at the WI accompanied by Cleopatra's hairdresser dressed up with a bird on her head. I cleared up the mess, hit the dog with Sue's toilet brush totally temporarily forgetting my promises to God, and got into Doris the Morris, distracting Sue by asking about her new cork sheets, which block out disturbances from ley lines.

'And I'm still on my psychic diet of course,' she added, glaring at the dog. She said that the entire procedure depended on her making her aura thinner by bombarding it with the colour red. First she'd had three baths in cranberry juice, which stained so much that she emerged looking like a mahogany commode. Then she had added cochineal to her drinks and gone to bed on red flannel sheets surrounded by flickering red candles on every surface. Perce had got into bed firmly convinced all of this was going to give him detached retinas but he woke up in the dead of the night to find Sue lying next to him with an anglepoise lamp firmly clamped between her thighs and a red bulb trained on her problem area, while on her head a large pair of earphones blasted out the bass line of a Meatloaf single. Choosing to ignore the lamp for now, he wisely asked her why she was listening to that appalling din in the night.

Sue said, though, that her diet's eventual success largely depended on her ability to clear her mind through the use of loud music and concentration on her flabby aura. She spent the rest of the dawn hours stoically massaging her inner thigh with a bright red face cloth while Perce rolled over in a troubled sleep. Sue reached into her glove compartment and got out a large box of Thornton's Continental selection.

'The worst thing about dieting I find,' she mused, 'is the boredom of it all. Have a choccie, we're almost there.'

Having sung three choruses of 'I Vow to Thee My Country' to get ourselves in the mood, when we arrived we were stunned to discover something unusual going on in the WI meeting hall—a row!

A very tall lady with round glasses—who looked a little like an aged Lettuce Leaf, Ugliest Girl in the School—took us to one side and explained what had happened.

The week before, the local television station had spent time filming a charming documentary entitled 'Pickling in Kent', and all the WI ladies had been enlisted for an on-screen pickle-off. The winner of the prize for the best pickle or chutney in the county would win a month's free hairdressing from Nigel de Canterbury, a floor-length fun fur from Alder's in Sevenoaks, and a week's holiday in Cheam.

'But,' continued our guide, who was called Ellie Clough-Winterlude, 'the rules seem to have been misunderstood by one of our ladies. Mrs Trent, over there in the floral dress and brown sandals, thought that only a fully matured chutney could be entered, whereas Mrs Rollins thought that only one actually made on camera could be exhibited. Of course she was bound to lose, because a pickle really needs to age and mature, don't you agree?' Sue and I nodded furiously.

'I always like mine to mature from one Christmas to another,' added Sue as I swung around with my neck like a walnut whip to make sure I didn't miss the next massive fib she told.

'The newly made pickle had no hope of winning and now Mrs Trent has just said that she's going home to pack for her week's holiday in Cheam and poor Mrs Rollins became rather belligerent.'

Belligerent? At that point Mrs Rollins was vibrating, berating Mrs Trent as a cheating hussy and flapping the edges of her apron at her as if she were performing some kind of ritualistic tribal dance.

'I've been a member of the Institute since 1942,' Ellie whispered as the two women continued to harangue each other and the word 'cheat' floated into the rafters. 'It was very different then. We always seemed to be digging for victory and were endlessly having knitting parties to make "comforts" for the soldiers. The WI knitted 1,284 pairs of mine sweeper gloves and more than 2,000 balaclavas, you know. That isn't to be sniffed at, is it? I even used to crochet curtains, although they did drop terribly in the middle. We were glad to get nice nylon ones by the end of the war. The institute used to be supportive for women in rural areas; now its image has changed. Ladies never fought and squabbled like this then.'

All of this completely satisfied Sue and me. This was exactly how we'd hoped it was going to be—aprons flapping and voices raised over a trip to Cheam. It was only a matter of time before we were clasped to the vast collective bosom of the Women's Institute and they began to impart their vast knowledge of stuffing, potting and broiling to us both.

'Still,' continued Ellie, fetching us both another cup of tea and three Jammie Dodgers, 'I think it's good for new members to see this sort of thing as it shows them we're not just a lot of old ladies obsessed with jam-making. We care passionately about pickling, too.'

We said goodbye to everyone and promised to be there again next week. 'Oh, you mustn't miss it,' said one elderly lady in a pale pink cardigan. 'We've got a guest speaker giving a talk—"Doilies through the Ages" ...'

CHAPTER 8

The Fete At Last

THE ANNUAL FETE is normally expected to make good the anticipated shortfall in the church fund collections. The collection itself is an infallible measure of the current state of parish politics, if not piety. It rises and falls according to the ebb and flow of ecclesiastical passion that is the mainstay of parish life and is most usually occasioned by the push and pull of High and Low Church and their separate adherents.

This unbridgeable divide—the cause of civil war and painful schism—was enacted weekly by the Compton Pauncefoot Church Committee, itself more political than the most politically correct of left-wing councils. Cardinal Wolsey could reincarnate and find himself elected 'chair' without obvious discomfort, the centuries having passed like a five-minute nap. The Vicar manfully, if wearily, straddled both camps, but his every appearance was the occasion of audible Low Church nose-twitching as his cassock billowing in his wake cast forth suspect wafts of idolatrous papist incense.

The Fete Committee is an offshoot of the Church Committee, and this year it was particularly troubled. There would be no need for the normally interminable discussions as to how the projected fete income would be spent. The tower, the last remaining of the original two, was clearly crumbling. It had been decided that bell-pulling should be reduced to a modest two tugs, barely enough to tinkle the welcome bell at weddings, and pipsqueak compared to the great two-tonners in the tower loft which had manfully boomed forth their muezzin call the past thousand years.

Mr Toper, the veteran pullist, as he insisted on being called, objected to the relevant parties in a written memo which he then copied to the Prime Minister and the Archbishop of Canterbury. He wrote that he had pulled continuously for twenty-five years and that if anyone could determine the potential amount of crumble per dong it was he—and he had never been consulted. He objected to some 'star chamber-like decision' to reduce his pulling to two dongs on the 'sub-bell' and criticised the typical 'fascist toady-like' manner in which the Vicar had accepted this recommendation without demur. Without even a by-your-leave or an official letter, Mr Toper had been informed of the decision the following Sunday by a curt command: 'Two pulls from now on, Mr Toper.'

The Prime Minister thanked Mr Toper for his letter;

the Archbishop, the Vicar and the committee ignored it. Mr Toper resigned shortly afterwards when Nigel, the altar boy, introduced his mother to him at the Co-op domestic toiletries counter as 'Ol' Two Pulls Toper'.

The story does not end there, however. Just as the peal of bells will ring ever out and further on in increasing waves of rippling sound, so too the consequences of that unfortunate letter were to have unforeseen and continuing repercussions throughout the glorious summer. No one could have suspected, as they sat down at the Grand Session of the Church Committee, the Fete Committee and its subsidiary the Fete Celebrity Committee, what was about to happen.

So many people had gathered in the lodge adjacent to the church, and it was so stiflingly hot, that several dissidents suggested we move the meeting outdoors, on to the grass. Typically, we had to vote on this motion first, and then, while the church wardens dealt with this unusual circumstance, various members, rudderless without their agenda, hung about outside sucking on cigarettes, which were now forbidden within the committee rooms. The younger ones opened their shirt fronts and lay on the grass; the women tucked their skirts modestly behind their knees. It was generally agreed that the sun was the best thing for the 'bones' and a sovereign remedy for angina, rheumatics and the vapours. At the same time one couldn't be too careful, the sun being noticeably 'thinner' that year over Compton Pauncefoot. Mr Green remarked how he had given up his allotment on account of the rise in sea levels on the estuary, and that he anticipated that his plot would be submerged 'within five year'. As he didn't fancy the taste of underwater beetroot, he was buggered if he was going to sweat every weekend for a patch of seaweed.

Mr Green looked sourly in the direction of Len Turner, the town grouch, whose 'silly bugger' had been just as audible as intended.

Lowther, still pink, subsided on to the grass next to Laurence and Karen Young. Karen is the captain of the Compton Pauncefoot ladies' netball team, which is very popular and attracts huge crowds, mainly of admirers of Karen's curvaceous bottom and rustling knickers.

On the left side of the lodge gate it was noticeable that heated debate was being enacted next to ranking officers of the Committee. 'Not now, not now Lowther, keep it for the meeting,' Laurence Young, ever the diplomat, could be heard saying loudly to Lowther, who had gone a delicate shade of fuchsia.

'I'll not be silenced in my fight against the man who wants to put votive candles into our church,' Lowther was muttering. 'An' he was definitely burnin' sommat last week, everyone could smell it.'

The Chairman of the Fete Committee rapped smartly on the table in front of him and the meeting was called to order.

The first thing to be discussed in great depth was where the funds should go. Was everyone definitely in favour of using fete funds to restore the tower? Or perhaps it could be considered, the Vicar had immediately chimed in, that the tower could be kept in its present state for another year as a historical monument? A bit of crumbling plaster can often be of added interest to scholars of the period, especially when combined with the obvious appeal of our flying buttresses.

Millicent harrumphed gently next to me, and whispered in a dreadful stage whisper, 'He wants the money to go for his blasted shower unit, and a big frilly lilac curtain. I've heard he's got his eye on the Pilgrim's Bathroom Centre in Dover.'

The Vicar eyed her across the lawn, and continued. 'It has just been brought to my attention that some council members and friends of the parish feel it may be worth us looking into the possibility of a study to see if we could persuade the tower to lean over. I'm sure everyone would agree it would make a real moneyspinner for the area.'

Karen stood up, and said that as chairperson of the Fete Celebrity Committee she was glad to announce that Daniel Day-Lewis had felt he had to decline their kind offer for him to open the fete, despite the obvious public relations advantages such an honour naturally bestowed on him. This meant that all the posters for the fete had to go to the printers with a large question mark above a silhouette, actually of Ralph, and 'Mystery Guest Star' underneath.

'Who's openin' the damn thing then?' someone shouted from the back.

Karen adjusted her netball skirt, which she was still wearing from her lunchtime game, and pursed her lips in a rather prim fashion. 'I know that everyone is going to be relieved to know that we have managed, despite such short notice, to confirm the acceptance of a local luminary, Miss Dot Babcock.'

The Vicar gazed at her in a glazed way.

'And because of this I've arranged for extra security from members of the Rotary Club, to prevent a crush of admirers.'

'Who is she?' yelled Len Turner.

'Yeah, who is she, this Babcock woman?' shouted a lanky farm boy who'd just been cycling past but had propped his bike up next to the laburnum tree when he saw the crowd, in case it was a rave party.

Karen drew herself up to her full height of five foot three and continued patiently, 'Miss Dot Babcock is a well-known local poet, who has been published three times in the *Woman's Realm* and has had several rejection slips from the *Sunday Times*, no less.'

'Well she'll pack 'em in,' called a man from the back of the lodge. 'Good job we didn't ask Madonna to come.'

The Vicar stood up hastily and said that he was thrilled that with such painfully short notice the fete celebrity committee had as usual come up trumps with a unique combination of glamour and literary talents.

'She's not glamorous,' said Lowther loudly. 'I've seen her in the garden centre buying slug pellets, and she's sixteen stone if she's a pound. And she wears one of them surgical stockings on one leg all the time.'

The Vicar ignored him pointedly, further enraging Lowther, so that his skin once more lit up like Blackpool Illuminations.

'An' I resign,' he shouted.

'Come, come, I think that's over-reacting a bit just

because Miss Babcock isn't one of the supermodels,' argued the Vicar, quite obviously taken by surprise.

'I'm resignin' because of that letter that Two Pulls Toper wrote anyways. No one's going to call me a Hitler just because I don't want the tower to fall on us all.'

The Vicar suddenly turned into a vicar and started saying 'Quite, quite' over and over again, wringing his hands in a distressed way.

'It's because of the votive candles and the incense and that fourteen-fold amen we had Sunday week,' whispered Laurence Young to me sotto voce.

'I'm resignin' as church warden an' that's the end of it,' snapped Lowther as he stormed off in the direction of the potting shed, head held high, the string around his trousers flapping in the light summery breeze.

After the meeting of the fete bigwigs, a lot of people spent their time moaning that the variety show in the Nissen hut had been cancelled. I was sad too, as I think any kind of show like that is a good place to study British character at work. More than anything else, it shows our great ability to make do. One memorable *Aladdin* conjured up all the seductive qualities of the East with the Vicar's samovar, while the Dance of the Seven Veils was performed with only the aid of a cut-up hammock and three sequins.

When we first moved to Compton Pauncefoot we saw a thousand-voice choir perform, but once we were in the town hall it became apparent there were only seventy-two of them present. Efforts had been made to pad them out by hiring rather low-cut nun's habits and making them all stand precariously perched on a fifteen-foot-

high scaffold. As they launched into a spirited rendition
of 'Ave Maria' [which according to my programme was
about to segue into 'Ain't No Mountain High Enough'],
the nun standing on the edge of the podium fainted and
plummeted straight down, breaking her fall on a rather
dusty yucca plant. Having spent so long arranging
everything for the show, the town choirmaster, a roofer
named Ted Bates, could be heard bellowing 'Keep singing, you stupid buggers' from the side of the stage,
upsetting several members of the church sewing circle
quite badly.

The great day approached and the Vicar looked much
happier, although things had not improved in his
relations with Lowther. Every time the Vicar crossed
the lawn, Lowther glared at him and immediately went
off in the opposite direction, mumbling under his
breath about imagery, the Virgin and various other ills.

'Is he all right?' panted the Vicar throwing himself on
to the grass and picking a fleck of cow-pat off one leg.
'Although he blames the letter Toper wrote about the
blasted bells for it all, he's been very odd with me too.'

I said I had no idea and changed the subject, asking
after the imminent fete and its many attractions.

'Well, as always there's good news and bad. The good
news is that Lowther has agreed to be in charge of the
public address system making announcements and playing cheering music all day. Miss Carlton-Mount has

promised to "man" the kissing booth, although her mother says she can't stand for more than an hour at a time because they've got varicose veins in the family, and the Sittingbourne Ukrainian Folklore Dance Group are going to dance while Dot Babcock cuts the ceremonial ribbon. All I'm praying for is really good weather on the big day.'

The day of the fete was perfectly delightful. Sunshine beamed into my window especially early, and loud trilling met my ears. I could also hear loud screeching as the starling's nest next to my window was still packed with hungry young who seemed to spend their whole summer eating and puking on to the new paintwork.

Lowther was obviously thrilled with his special duties. He had been thoroughly testing the PA system since about ten past seven that morning, so that when I finally made it downstairs in the sprigged nightie I've had since I was twelve—the one with the indelible egg stains down the front—I noticed that the various members of the Rotary Club who'd been put in charge of security were now swinging their mallets in time to 'Mud's Greatest Hits'. When I saw that they were stringing off an enclosure for the grand opening, I suggested to Lowther that perhaps he'd like to broaden his musical horizons for a couple of minutes, so then we had 'Una Paloma Blanca' so that helpers erected their stalls as they fought an irresistible urge to prance around their handbags.

I came out of the house to find the Vicar standing on the mounting stairs surveying the scene, dressed in a rather bright pair of Bermuda shorts printed with beaming sharks that had bubbles coming out of their mouths saying 'Aloah'. By this time, men were busy all over the paddock, stringing up miles and miles of Union Jack bunting left over from VE day; others struggling with the origami-like complications of ancient trestle tables. A minute podium stood in the centre of the paddock, where a group of teenagers under threat of death were removing the worst of the sheep droppings, and another group, stripped to the waist, was hauling at the guy ropes of the marquee, which kept toppling over on to its side so that the Vicar had almost despaired of his flower-arranging contest running smoothly.

I made tea for as many men as I had mugs for, and handed one to the Vicar who was peering nonchalantly into a large box of second-hand books and had already pocketed *Angelique in Exile* and a Georgette Heyer. By now Lowther had grown tired of the cacophony of seventies hits and temporarily slipped out of the tank top and platform boots he'd been wearing in his dreams, and was shouting 'One TWOOO, TWOOO, TWOOO' into the microphone, as though he was the sound man on a Led Zeppelin world tour.

In order to pass the time until Dot arrived for the great opening, I took the children for a walk down the lane to the lake where local fishermen wait all day for frightening-looking carp and pike to appear out of its depths. Some of these fish have been so large that they could quite easily have rocked a small boat or eaten a large wader, but no accidents have occurred so far. As I watch them patiently fishing, their hats tipped over their faces to protect them from the glare, I always think that I would never eat such an ugly fish, especially one which looked as if it had spent its entire life consuming a diet of unspeakable things.

Already there were patches of lesser bindweed appearing around the lake, a few tiny wild cherries and—most impressive of all—the little rose haws that are known locally as Heavenly pears, much to Heavenly's delight. As we wandered on, looking for blackberries and refusing to admit that we were still too early for them to have ripened, we passed the old gravel pits. Next door was the delicious Gothic cottage where three brothers live.

The Watson Boys are charmers to a man despite their old and gnarled appearance; to small children I am sure they seem perfectly Shakespearean, with their velvet caps and large hats [one of which has a feather in it]. Despite their odd appearance, they are the envy of the area.

The cottage, for a start, is supremely pretty. Painted with a sweet pink wash, it is based on Horace Walpole's design for Strawberry Hill and was built in the nineteenth century by the gravel pit owner who wanted a building that would be the envy of passing travellers. Even today, its arches and oriental battlements along the roof and its little quatrefoil windows force the weariest traveller to look again.

Whenever out for a walk in the area, we always have to stop and peer over the fence. Although it must seem nosy to anyone living in a town, we can't resist. The children always want to eat the huge peaches the brothers grow in their little green house and admire the feathers in their hats and their general air of exoticism. I have to admire their tiny thatched Gothic folly, which I long to steal in the night.

But back to local envy. It is because of their gardening talents and their green fingers that they are viewed with some dislike. Every year at the Harvest Festival, their marrow is the one most likely to break the steps up to the altar, and at the annual Vegetable and Fruit contest grown men have virtually despaired of ever matching their mammoth tubers and mutant runner beans.

The children said good morning to the Watsons, gratefully receiving their peaches in return, and I asked after their onion—which is like a fourth member of the family—and heard it was 'feeling tip top today'. We bade them farewell and went back to the fete preparations.

By twelve o'clock everything was ready to begin. Miss Carlton-Mount, a plumpish girl in a tiara and a vast puce sweatshirt and matching jeans, was waiting on the kissing stall. Guess the Weight of the Pig had been set up on the opposite side of the paddock to avoid confusion, and the bring and buy, bottle and book stalls were neatly lined up on the uneven ground. Inside the candy-striped marquee the various entrants had already carefully positioned their arrangements for the flower-arranging prize. I asked Lowther, who had developed a sore throat and was having a few moments off from his impassioned rendition of 'Ob-la-di Ob-la-da' over the loudspeakers, what he was entering this year.

'Got these blasted themes this year. All the Vicar's idea, so you can bet it's something he's heard about from Rome.'

'What kind of themes?' I enquired.

'Themes,' he replied flatly, 'two themes. One is Starbursts on Velvet which Cedric saw in a magazine in the health centre when he had that ingrowing toe nail done. The other one is Swallows and Amazons. I can't see any self-respecting man doing this women's stuff, so I'm just entering three lupins in the domestic lupin section this year, and that big purple primula that Honey tried to eat last week.'

Dot Babcock arrived in the Vicar's car. She'd obviously been driven far too fast with the top down as she looked like an Afghan hound as she teetered out on her high heels.

The crowds good-naturedly cheered as she approached the podium to hear the Vicar's speech about the fete and its aims. Unfortunately just before she sat down her spiked heel trod firmly on a missed sheep dropping. It attached itself firmly to her foot, so that throughout the speech and her eventual moment of glory cutting the ribbon she was shaking her foot furiously trying to dislodge the offending item, much to the amusement of the cub photographer from the local paper who was busily snapping her. She finally removed it by dragging her foul-smelling heel along the grass, but not before three rolls of film had been taken of her standing on one leg like a visiting stork.

Sue and I rushed off to buy up any lime green matinee jackets with matching bobble hats we might have missed on our weekly forays to the WI. Sue also bought a decanter for fifty pence, and a large rubber chicken-shaped hot water bottle. I was just buying a batch of meltingly fragrant flapjacks when I spotted Mrs Trent nose to nose with her old adversary Mrs Rollins who was loudly accusing her of falsifying jam for the fete.

'I saw her, I did,' she said loudly as a small crowd of interested local matrons gathered around clutching their macramé pot holders. 'I saw her buying that exact jam at the Co-op and I'd be willing to swear on our Ern's life that she has just stuck it into that homemade pot, I bet. She's always been a madam, that one. I haven't forgotten that pickle.'

This was getting boring, rather like one of Honey and Harmony's arguments which stretch on for days of You-did-I-didn't-You-did-I-didn't-ing. I wandered away to view the beaming babies entering the Beautiful Baby contest. The Vicar had sensibly made sure there was a prize for everybody who entered—Best Feet, Cutest Nose and even Most Charming Chin.

The only thing marring the perfection of the day was Lowther. Along with announcing events, playing early seventies Abba hits, and singing along tunelessly with 'Dancing Queen', he was now berating the Vicar over the loudspeaker, saying he was taking too long in judging things. Could he get a move on as it'd be dark by the time he'd judged the baby contest—either that or they'd all have gone to university.

As he roared laughing at his own joke, the familiar strains of Abba floated over the loudspeakers. Sue groaned. 'I can't stand that Swedish stuff, you know, probably because I was once Queen Christina, you know,' she told me, cramming two of my flapjacks into her mouth at once.

I noted she wasn't on the diet any more, and she told me that she'd given it up as life was too short to live in such utter misery and starvation. 'I am a woman with a woman's needs,' she said rather grandly. All that had happened was that she'd become obsessed with food and had suddenly noticed quite how much money Pizza Hut was spending on advertising.

Our conversation was terminated when she suspected some kind of contact coming through from Mary Queen of Scots. Lately she longed for everything tartan she saw in the shops and had even felt herself beckoned by a 'soul in torment' to buy three tartan picture frames in Laura Ashley that morning.

Slowly the crowds dispersed, and everything was gradually packed up while my children scuttled around eating anything left over on the stalls.

Dot was driven off by the Vicar, clutching a bottle of sherry and waving furiously out of the window, and the WI cleared their stalls efficiently, with Mrs Moss washing up in the sheep trough while the photographer from the local paper took idyllic pictures of the delightful rural scene.

I should have known better. A couple of days later Cedric came round to borrow a tea bag, and brought the paper with him. The headline rose before me massively. 'FETE LIVER FLUKE SCARE, THOUSANDS IN TERROR'—'I hope none of us gets mad sheep's disease' it quoted a local mother, as she clutched her child to her bosom.

The report about the fete mentioned none of the summer glories of the fete, but focused on two un-fortunate aspects of the event: Mrs Moss washing up the tea things up in the sheep trough, risking possible death to tens of thousands of tea drinkers; and the donkey rides which, due to the heat, ended up not as a circuit of the lawn but as a ten-step walk in a small tight circle before the donkey dropped to its knees, exhausted. The Vicar was loath to lower the price of this exciting ride from its usual fee of ten pence, but eventually when he realised rides were lasting less than fourteen seconds in the midday afternoon heat, he was forced to cave in and halve the price, the paper reported gleefully.

CHAPTER 9

Pick Your Own

ONE OF THE MOST DELICIOUS OCCUPATIONS of the summer holidays is a trip to the local Pick Your Own farm owned by Violet and Abby Sourbutt and Violet's son Reg. It is also a good way of keeping the children and all their friends occupied for a whole day when the pleasures of hanging upside down in a tree are starting to wane. It is perfect—they are outside, at one with nature, and I don't have to cook for any of them once we get home because it's hard to have room for real food when you've just consumed fourteen pounds of over-ripe strawberries lying face down in a boiling hot field all day long.

So the week after the fete, when even more unadulterated excitement was called for, I piled everyone into the car eating toppling ice creams, which dribbled incessantly on to the seats, down fat chins and stuck to fat tummies and thighs.

'If you don't stop dribbling, wasps will attack us,' I barked. Both of the little ones immediately started to cry, because a wasp got up the leg of Honey's shorts last week and she almost died of shock.

'We'll stop at the pond and you can wash the sticky stuff off,' I continued as the sniffling abated slightly. Like clockwork Harmony started to blub at the thought of water on her body, like the witch in *The Wizard of Oz*.

As always we were accompanied by Harmony's two great friends Simon and Tom, sons of Karen and Laurence. Tom was gazing pensively out of the window concentrating on some piece of technical drawing he was planning to execute later on. Harmony and Simon concentrated on thinking of rhymes for bum and willie for a song they were composing together—it completely ignored iambic pentameters, and appeared to have more verses than *The Ancient Mariner*.

Honey, having been washed off with a damp bulrush, and Heavenly, having been chased by a swan, were soon dozing fitfully in the back of the car. The rabbit was, as always, sandwiched in a necklock between them, dreaming of death as he must view each day with trepidation from his little pink handbag. I produced a large bag of toffees, which meant the car was immediately filled with the horrible sound of chewing. I could see why couples divorce after thirty years of marriage, and then, when asked why, reply that they couldn't stand the sound of chewing any more...

There is now a great deal of fierce competition between the various farms on the Pick Your Own scene around here, so the farm where we Pick Our Own has added an adventure playground [albeit a suitably rustic one] and a farmyard corner with a number of appealing furry animals. Children can buy bags of food for them, then spend the afternoon alternately petting and being savagely nipped by these beasts.

As I paid for six bags of goat-rabbit-calf-piglet food at the door, a huge pig lay on her side in the slippery mud and her massive litter played in the dirt around her, sunning their tiny bodies, filthy all over except for deliciously pink, perfectly shiny little snouts that rose and fell delicately as they snored around their massive mother. Then suddenly, as one, they leaped to their feet and launched themselves at her body, desperate to feed, climbing over one another to get a good position, scuffling and nipping and then lining up like kids for school dinners.

Next door, a large pen held a hugely built pig, who was the father of the squalling mass next door. He stood majestically in the muck, surveying the scene, casting a hostile eye towards Heavenly who immediately hid behind my skirts and dropped all her piglet food in terror. Honey was howling in the distance—one of the rabbits had bitten her and was hanging on to her finger as she attempted to shake it off. Harmony, happy for once, merely hung upside down off a log, twenty feet up in the air, on the army assault course which paraded as a climbing frame.

It was time to move on to the picking fields, and lie

142

among the little green leaves, searching their dark
hidden depths for ripe fruit. As we turned to leave, the
gigantic pig, angry at Heavenly leaving without scrap-
ing up her dropped morsels and feeding him, suddenly
made a ferocious bellowing noise and ran at the fence,
clearing the one between him and the rest of his family
in one bound, and running through the next one before
stopping at a screeching halt right behind us. I was so
shocked I gave him my wallet and we ran for the fields,
leaving the farmer to round up his recalcitrant pig by
banging on a steel bucket next to his ears. Something
I'm used to at our house.

We spent the rest of the afternoon picking the soft
fruit. I managed to fill several little willow baskets
although I kept falling asleep in the shade with the baby.
Simon, Tom and Harmony held a competition to see
who could invent the crudest lyrics to 'I'm Too Sexy'. I
made them go down to the other end of the field. The
children happily filled no punnets, but ate pounds and
pounds of fruit. I imagined they would probably have
to spend the night welded to the toilet.

I watched Honey wandering down the rows of
bushes, her perfect little fingers occasionally darting
down under the leaves to snatch up the ripe fruit and
cram it into her perfect little mouth. Her skin was
lightly burnished to a dull golden colour and her
matted golden hair fell over her face, stained with the
juice which had run in rivulets down her chin and
down her little chest. She was the prettiest thing in the
whole panorama of nature, fragrantly living up to her
name. I sat up slightly dizzy from the heat and the

unexpected sleep, and ran over to kiss her and bite her neck which was scented with fruit.

When we arrived home I saw Lowther putting the door back on to its hinges and hammering a new piece of wood across the bottom where the thieves had broken the door in. The crime wave was continuing as the summer stretched on, and the culprits still had not been found – all suspects had turned out to be red herrings. A couple of days before, our *replacement* garden seat had disappeared.

'Tom's been told 'e's got to go under cover, you know,' Lowther told me with his mouth full of nails. 'Tonight it's to be, in that nightclub place in Duck Lane in Canterbury.'

I pointed out that this was hardly a covert operation if he knew the exact time and place of the assignation.

'Well,' he continued looking sheepish, 'it's only me as knows. Tom's been a bit worried about going in that nightclub—'e can't stand that sort of thing. He thought that, seeing as how I enjoy music so much, I could come with him an' keep an eye on things.'

I told him I couldn't wait to hear how it all went.

'We've been told to blend in you know,' he said, resuming his hammering...

In the kitchen, the fruit in the punnets was covered with feasting flies, which made me feel a bit ill. I decided to make a very complicated but beautiful-looking toffee-cake-based pavlova that I'd seen in *Good Housekeeping*. It was the sort of thing women in the WI make in ten minutes without a Moulinex, whisking their egg whites with a bent coathanger, but sadly mine came out very flat like a cream-covered whoopee cushion. It tasted rather delicious, but looked so repulsive that it made me feel depressed. At teatime I rallied and blamed the excessive use of pink lights in food photographs.

'And,' I said airily to my husband, who was chewing desperately at my rubbery meringue like a prize bullock, 'they actually use mashed potato in all those photos, not real cream...'

'Hmmm,' he responded wearily, 'I wish you had too.'

It had been quite late when we had finally got home, so the children for once had been glad to go to bed, leaving me to make my excuses about my pudding-making capabilities. It was to be a busy night. No sooner had I sat down but Lowther walked in wearing a brand new pair of blue jeans with razor sharp creases ironed into the middle. He'd just bought them at Millet's.

As we'd been in nightclubs in the past, he wanted to ask us whether we thought this was suitable for the undercover assignation he and Tom were going on that night. Lowther looked around the drawing room furtively as he tugged at the stiff blue jeans which seemed to be chaffing him somewhat.

As soon as he had vanished into the darkness Dorcas came over. She flung herself on to the sofa, catapulting several cushions on to the floor like a circus act.

'I had to come over, otherwise I was so bored I

thought I might end up ringing Loveday,' she told me. 'He's not rung since that night, you know, so I feel I'll have to call him.'

'Don't,' I said shortly.

'I know, I know,' she said. 'Those crush-type calls always end in such abject humiliation. You keep the phone ringing throughout the whole of *Juliet Bravo*, and then his mother answers and involves you in a long conversation about the dog's glands. Alternatively you keep it ringing seventy times till he picks it up and answers every conversational gambit with an unintelligible one-word reply, while the sounds of a good party waft from the background, and every word is interrupted by a party popper hitting the receiver. I know, you're right, I shouldn't ring him. It'll only end with me rolling off the sofa and trying to chew the carpet. I'm so embarrassed.'

'Yup,' I said trying to watch the TV and be sympathetic.

'Gorrrd,' she replied. 'If I'd known how boring you were going to be I'd have gone out with Lowther to the nightclub.' Wiping her nose, she stuffed two punnets of strawberries into her bag and went home.

I was dozing in the garden the next morning, exhausted from my efforts picking flowers; a large basket full of cut blooms lay next to me, and my hat was discarded somewhere else entirely. I was eminently suitably clad in an old Victorian wedding dress my father had bought in an auction when he actually thought he was bidding for a sage green bidet and sink set. As I lay there, it appeared that the modern world and all of its multiple horror had receded into the ether.

I was brought back to earth with a bang as Lowther tumbled into view, looking pale and drawn. What had happened to his usual healthy oak-apple tan?

'It were a terrible night,' he assured me, sitting down unexpectedly next to me on the tartan car rug I'd spread out for the children. 'Ar, a night of horror, in fact, in that club place.'

I had no idea that Canterbury held such dens.

'It were awful,' he added.

Prior to his night of horror it seemed that all of Lowther's vague impressions of nightclubs had been gleaned from old Fred Astaire films and a matinée performance of *Saturday Night Fever* he'd been dragged along to by a niece of thirteen. As he'd been expecting a hybrid of the two it was no shock to discover that the dark, dank red-plush interior of Luv Gun II wasn't quite what he'd anticipated. Nor, it seemed, had he expected Tom to be taking his instructions to blend in so seriously.

He'd been hoping to shuffle away quietly in a darkened corner, occasionally breaking off to scan the room for the lawnmower thieves. Perhaps they'd be standing by the bar with a beer in one hand and a strimmer in the other? Lowther had never been so arrogant as to imagine that his own rather unique sense of rhythm would coincide with that of Tom's or whoever else he found himself dancing with.

He was just settling into a dance very similar to the one Prince Charles always does with Maori tribesmen when Tom suddenly started pointing at the light bulbs and bellowing various lyrics, before attempting a triple-toe-loop salchow ending with the splits on the four-foot-square dance floor, which unfortunately resulted in him tearing his regulation dark blue serge trousers at the same time.

The evening wore on, and more and more half-naked youths crowded around them, sweating profusely and drinking potent drinks in small containers. It became apparent that, in the interests of blending in, Tom had also drunk one too many gin and guava juices and he kept toppling over, losing his balance.

Cross, and with a burgeoning headache, Lowther went and sat near the exit to inhale a few draughts of fresh air, praying the mission would soon be over and he could come home. Unfortunately, Tom was traversing the club in a conga with two agricultural students and a Rastafarian who'd missed the last train home and had 'Yo Bum' tattooed on his forehead.

Lowther dozed slightly, but suddenly awoke with his head jerking up, the way it always does on crowded commuter trains when you start snoring. He looked around the club and realised that Tom had vanished, and was worried that the gang had spotted him and hauled him off somewhere to be lawnmown over.

It transpired that after his fourteenth Love Bomb and his eighth gin and guava juice Tom had become violently sick. Worse still, the rather attractive girl he'd tried to make an impression on during the evening was now standing outside the cubicle as he alternated between being sick and resting his hot head on the cool tiles. He then realised he had a worse problem, and tried to undo the belt of his uniform trousers in the confined space. He wished he hadn't teamed them with the tie-dye smily-face tee-shirt, as the fringes kept getting stuck in the zip.

Torn, Tom shifted his position to accommodate this new attack down below, and threw up again. Suddenly everything became a terrifying blur, and, as he resumed his other position on the loo, he realised that, although he could dimly hear both Lowther and the very attractive blonde in a Lycra catsuit, he could see nothing.

It was then that he noticed that he'd dropped his glasses into the loo. He peered wearily but unhopefully into the bowl, vowing inwardly never to leave the station again, and never to pursue stolen goods as long as his career lasted.

He flushed his glasses away, and blindly opened the door to Lowther, who led him away into the darkness outside.

'And,' continued Lowther, 'it's the last time either of us ever drink a drop again. We virtually signed the pledge, we did, after last night.'

The next day Tom was cycling happily down the hill, wearing his spare glasses and happy with life [mainly because he could see again] when he spotted the unthinkable happening in broad daylight in the middle of Compton Pauncefoot. Two men were busily carrying a small ornamental fountain out of the front gates of a neighbouring house into an old van.

After the hell of the other night it must have seemed like a vision to Tom, who sensibly did nothing, but pelted along on his bike while the van chugged up the hill before stopping at a farm building three miles away. With admirable self-restraint, partly caused by the remnants of his hangover, he still did nothing, but when officers returned to the scene later, the barn was full of Compton Pauncefoot's prized implements, including a large ten-by-six sign of the Cinque Portes that had been missing from the Dover flyover for six months.

Even losing his glasses seemed worth it after this summer. He felt like Karl Malden in *The Streets of San Francisco*, not only arresting the Vicar but also this ...

AUTUMN

CHAPTER 10

Are You Sexy?
(Or: Tribulations In The Countryside)

In the olden days, autumn was a season fraught with superstitions around here—the locals were apparently scared to pick hazelnuts on a Sunday in case it was the devil holding down the boughs. For some reason they also were firmly convinced that Beelzebub lurked in the blackberry brambles—it was widely thought that on Michaelmas Day, having been thrown bodily out of heaven like Tom out of the Luv Gun II, he spent the rest of the day spitting on blackberries thus rendering them totally tasteless. If that's the theory, he's also spent the day spitting on most of the fruit stocked in urban supermarkets.

The blazing summer was slowly giving way, though not without a fight, to the golden transition of autumn, when the leaves turn gold and red and then drop, leaving a carpet of damp leaves on the ground in the woods, which Heavenly loved to lie in. There was little hope of Dorcas finding a tall dark handsome farmer at this time of the year, as every worker was busy with the harvest wheat and most fruits were busily being picked. Huge combine harvesters ploughed through the fields, cutting the stalks, cleverly separating the seeds and then tying the whole lot into bundles. A century ago this would have been done in picturesque toil by hand. I always yearn for a return to things like that, knowing that it's highly unlikely I'd be the one half-killing myself baling up straw by hand, but looking rustically pretty while I'm at it.

Harvest Festival is the main festivity with which the town celebrates its unity and continuity. This year, the schoolchildren were as excited as ever, all bringing to school tins of food which they then arranged in rather wobbly towers around the altar, ready to be sent to the local old people's alms houses in town after the service.

I set Harmony, Honey, Heavenly, Simon and Tom to work in the kitchen with a bundle of straw which we valiantly attempted to make into corn dollies. We finally grew tired of it, breaking off and littering the entire kitchen with seeds, and settled for plaiting it and then tying it around the church pews when no one was looking.

Millicent and some other ladies of the parish had made quite marvellous arrangements of flowers all over the church which is very plain inside. In earlier times it had marvellous frescoes which were painted over in whitewash by the Victorians who disapproved almost as much as Lowther and our current congregation of such fripperies and fancies in a place of worship. Lowther had added pots of lilies around the altar and as we all stood back to admire our handiwork we agreed that it both looked and smelled marvellous, even though Growler had been in earlier and salvaged some bread sheaves of corn that the local baker had carefully positioned all over the place.

The annual Vegetable and Fruit Contest was also held that week, and already the rumblings of terrible discontent could be heard echoing from the allotments as various brawny semi-clad men who had spent the best part of the year kissing and crooning to giant onions and marrows became worried about the arrival of the Watson brothers' entries.

The Nissen hut was again called into action as a venue for displaying all the vegetables. The only worry was voiced by the Vicar who hoped it wouldn't be like last year when a marrow had almost brought the double doors off their hinges as it was dragged in on a trolley. Sue and I went in to look at the exhibits. Beautiful blush pink peaches sat on a velvet cushion, three softly furry damsons were placed in tight symmetry on a doily and a number of Granny Smith's that looked as if they had been varnished were already wearing rosettes in the fruit section which ran straight down the left hand side of the hut.

But it was the vegetables that made people gasp. Harmony and Simon, who had broken off work on the operetta about farting they were now diligently composing in their den in the garden, came expressly to see the biggest pea. Merely saying this was enough to convulse them both with such hilarity that they had to go and rest outside with two ice lollies each.

There were leeks at least eighteen inches long, tomatoes like vast blood red melons, marrows the size of my children and onions so vast and round and pearly they seemed like small planets that had dropped out of the sky.

But none were wearing rosettes because entries had not closed and, like Frank Sinatra making a comeback for one year only, the Watson Boys were late, as late as they could be so that their onion—the onion that in another life would have become the fifth Beatle if they'd had anything to do with it—was at that moment enshrouded in a large scarf and being wheeled sedately up the road on a large trap led by their elderly pony, Sorrento.

'It ain't natural,' Len Turner muttered. 'They sleeps next to the damn thing. They take it in turns to put a blanket over it and sleep with it.'

'No,' said an old buffer who was holding his two entrants, a couple of ten-inch runner beans and a tomato that had sustained some kind of minor injury on the way there.

'Yes, they do. I been past at night, trying to have a quick look at the state of play, and they were sleeping with it!'

'And they give it Guinness three times a day too.'

'Nah, really?'

'And play it Matt Munro records.'

The Watsons finally breezed in, looking like out-of-work actors from a run-down touring group. One of them swept off the scarf, while the other two bowed low, doffing their hats at their assembled peers and turning theatrically to the onion which sat there on the barrow as big as a kennel and weighing at least seven stone.

'My God,' said Len. 'Thems bastards 'as done it again.'

'D'you think it's the beer or the Matt Munro records as does it?' said his friend shaking the Watson Boys' hands vigorously, as though some of their magical talents would rub off on him. After their inevitable but glorious victory, the Watsons wandered off into the dusk to prepare for next year's triumph, midges flying around them.

Central heating is frowned upon in old houses by many ancient families who have lived in their homes for centuries, getting by with one side lamp for fifteen bedrooms. Over the years they have adapted to the freezing cold and wear their overcoats to watch TV, only taking them off to eat formal dinners in dingy semi-darkness, so that now they view heating and sometimes even good plumbing with great suspicion.

In some of the bigger local houses the walls retain the cold so well, and have the added bonus of decades of damp, that thick thermal underwear is worn even in summer. It has the added advantage of doubling up as a kind of contraceptive. Despite Princess Diana's attempts to popularise both, it is impossible to be sexually aroused by anyone you've seen wearing thermal long johns or popsox. Popsox are the sort of things that Elizabeth Taylor wears with hotpants when she's going through one of her fat patches.

I digress. With the onset of autumn, the scions of these old families run as swiftly as Hiawatha through the corridors, plunging bravely through the damp gloom until they reach their destination. Then they throw themselves down in front of tiny hearths where three small mossy twiglets are fizzing doomily in the grate, providing a small pool of light—but no heat.

It is these same people who always look askance when you tell them that you are thinking of modernising your heating. They mutter, 'You aren't giving up real fires, are you?' as though you are suddenly planning to spend all evening looking at a new radiator.

Unfortunately, putting in new heating or modernising old is so hugely expensive that most people simply have to make do, and wear layers of horrible garments designed to make anyone with any sense of vanity almost suicidal with despair. Our own turn-of-the-century system was so expensive to run that we suspected that it was operated by vestal virgins on bikes, pedalling furiously to give us our meagre energy supply. Despite vast fuel bills, it barely gave us enough heat to survive.

A little man from Canterbury came round to inspect the system. He said what the Priory really needed was a factory-sized boiler with forty million btu's, whatever that meant—my husband nodded knowledgeably, so I refrained from asking. With delight he added, 'You know, it's costin' you forty pounds every time you have a bath!'

Immediately all baths were banned until further notice by Husband, whose last bath was five years ago and was such a big family event we took more polaroids of it than we did of the last baby being born. Harmony, of course, was delighted. She is continually trying to bring back the grey tide mark around the neck as a fashion statement.

The little man said he could try to do a bit of tinkering, and he did so, furiously wiggling knobs and peering with his torch at the various dials and scales all over our present boiler, which was put into the house at the turn of the century and weighs more than three double decker buses. He also tapped on all of the pipes, hit the radiators with a small hammer like the one doctors use to test the reflexes on your knees and tried to squeeze himself around the back of the washing machine for fifteen minutes.

Then he rode off again on his bike, leaving my husband head in hands on the kitchen table forbidding the entire family to ever bath again before stumbling off to find solace in the library with the *Spectator* and a ginger cake from the WI.

One of the disadvantages of living in the country is the fear that sets in whenever a domestic disaster occurs—

you never know how long it's going to take that repair man to arrive, and that's only if you've been lucky enough to find one who actually answers his phone.

So you can imagine my alarm when a combination of things resulted in a catastrophe the next day. Firstly, the central heating man and his spanner must have caused some damage as he lurked at the back of the washing machine. Then a disposable nappy got into the laundry and disappeared unseen into the machine. And then, since our pipes had been assaulted, the house had been like a furnace, with water steaming out of the taps like molten lava.

This must have melted something inside the Candy Puff-O-Matic, because when I opened the door of our ancient washing machine this morning, water poured at high velocity all over the kitchen floor. Throbbing crashing waves drenched me as I fought bravely to shut the porthole until finally I gave up and resigned myself to the grey lukewarm water that was eddying around my feet and worryingly pouring towards the rather quaint runners along the cloisters. It was not easy to try and erect a Thames barrier out of three socks, several old tissues and the ripped five-pound note I found floating in the dingy brew, although I did notice with interest that the Queen's portrait had now soaked up so much water she was resembling a manatee.

So I did what any other self-respecting housewife would have done in this domestic crisis. I threw all of the clean tea towels I'd just ironed on to the water, and leaped on them in a sort of frenzied flamenco. It did the trick— almost all the water was soaked up, and for once the kitchen floor looked rather attractive after its drowning. I realised that many things can go wrong in your life, but if your washing machine breaks down it can send you over the precipice into madness. So I rang the Potterton boiler representative, as they are the only plumbers within a ten-mile radius who always arrive quickly. A bugle sounded in the distance, he was on his way.

It's a fact of life in the country that, like shepherds and lonely cow-milkers toiling in the early hours of the morning, women living in rural areas see fewer people, and also very different people, than do their urban friends. What I'm actually saying is that you don't meet endless men in coffee bars at lunchtime, all flirting wildly with you. Instead you see a lot of other mothers picking up their children and talking about support tights, recommending which ones will stretch enough so that you can pull them up and use them as a combined girdle-catsuit and polo-neck if the weather gets nippy. You see the young sergeant and mainly notice that the worrying pustule he had on his neck has now spread over his face so that he looks like an illustration from *Dermatologist Monthly*. Suddenly you either: [1] start fancying lots of tradesmen; [2] find yourself wishing the Channel tunnel was open so there'd be even more men in Kent that you'd never be able to meet; or [3] you sit watching so much telly that you find yourself uncontrollably attracted to the man who does the traffic reports for the Sittingbourne area.

So, when the man from the boiler company arrived at four in the afternoon, I was unprepared for any excitement. Still in my bri-nylon baby-dolls and feeling as if

I'd been wearing them since my waters broke, I opened the door to be greeted by a youth of about nineteen with an unseasonably dark tan, which he told me he got on a bed 'darn the sports centre'. At this point I realised that there was no point in thinking about flirting because if he did so I'd know that someone else had walked into the room behind me and he'd be chatting to her. The only other thing I might be able to talk about was support tights because I can never remember what to say to men over four feet tall anyway, unless they'd like to chat about the new Masters of the Universe space cruiser attachment.

He stripped off his tee-shirt, revealing a back as brown and as tanned as the pouffe we brought back from Morocco last year. As he bent over the washing machine with his spanner sticking seductively out of his back pocket, he reminded me of a friend who, in a similar situation, leaped on to the plumber's back and frenziedly rode him into the bedroom, slapping his bottom with her washing-up squeegee.

All that happened to me was that he fixed the washing machine. As he was leaving, I fumbled in my purse for change, twittering horribly and aware that he was looking at my roots. He leaned louchely against the door frame and mumbled, 'You know sommat, your body's like my spanner.'

I paused in my search for tenpence and looked up at his beaming face.

'Yeah, it tightens my nuts,' he added, sauntering off to his little van delighted with himself ...

It was this single incident which led to my re-

-evaluation of things. Was living in the country making me lose my feminine mystique, I wondered to myself that evening, as I lay alone on the sofa with my Emerson Fittipaldi boilersuit and the pair of slippers shaped like two udders which I'd borrowed because I thought I was getting housemaid's knee on one toe. I flicked open a magazine, disturbed that rural life slackens one's feminine standards. Everyone in the countryside lives vicariously through *Cosmopolitan*. Articles such as 'Is the frankfurter fashionable?' and 'Better orgasms on your grant' are sandwiched between photos of girls with lips so glossy you could shine a Mazda coupé with them. And all the women wear underwired bras that turn their chests into shelves that they can rest male models on.

It seemed to me that my feminine mystique had first plummeted after having babies. The second you are put into that white hospital gown with a completely invisible bottom, it's hard to feel as if you are a throbbing love gusset. [My gown also had a large laundry mark across the front so that Heavenly thought my name was St Mary's for the first three days.]

I noticed that my magazine had thoughtfully provided a quiz with a checklist—Keeping Romance Alive:

· *Do you let him see you at your worst?*

The last time my husband saw me in something resembling women's clothing he had to be given mouth-to-mouth resuscitation on our sofa, followed by a swift slapping with a birch twiglet. My husband regularly gets to see me lying impatiently in a slick of shaved hairs as I make a policy of trying to entice the children into the weekly warm bath we're all allowed by sitting there the door wide open waiting for them to turn me into something like a cross between Kris Kristofferson and Santa with the aid of a can of menthol shaving cream and an old spatula.

· *Do you try to pretend that your husband is a stranger?*

This question baffled me so I had to switch on *Gardener's Question Time* to give myself time to think. With a discussion about growing fuchsias in the background, I asked myself whether it meant that we played sexy games where I had to pretend I was a traffic warden, and he was a combine harvester salesman? I wondered if the pair of furry rabbit ears I had left over from the Easter Egg Hunt counted for a point.

· *Do you make sure that you have some special time together?*

Currently I have so little time for anything that the kids' toe nails are in direct competition for a world record alongside those of Howard Hughes. I am rapidly turning into one of those old codgers who always lean over and ask 'What exactly is a gramophone record?' and the only kind of rapping I'm interested in is around a Chanel box.

· *Are you sexy?*

ARE YOU SEXY?

This seemed the most risky question of all. If I were to tog up in purple lace flying tackle and sashay around the TV set I would probably be told I was blocking the view of Glenn Hoddle's balls. Or otherwise be given the Spanish Inquisition about what I'd done that day, in case I'd broken the thermostat on the heating again twisting it all the way round.

Magazines like you to be 'inventive'—a women's-magazine euphemism for loads of different athletic positions in bed, impossible in the country because the air in everyone's bedroom is so cold that frostbite could ensue. Anyone contemplating being adventurous should simply look down into a mirror and be amazed at how they immediately resemble Richard Nixon.

Still, I thought that perhaps it was time for a night in a country-house hotel nearby, so I booked the Chilston Park Hotel complete with four poster, only to be told they couldn't do next weekend because the boiler had just flooded the kitchen and the chef was wearing waders...

CHAPTER 11

The Last Gymkhana Of The Season

DORCAS WAS ON THE DOORSTEP when I came downstairs. She'd just finished reading *Mandingo* and wanted to know if I'd like to borrow it.

'Really,' she said, handing me the book, 'what I liked most was that it was so much like real life.'

She was feeling this way because in order to cool her ardour over the poor boy from the hop farm she'd been having a brief fling with a waiter from a kebab café in the next town. She'd decided that, for once, she would attempt a strategy like playing hard to get. Dorcas normally consummated her romances after two hours watching Pearl and Dean commercials followed by half a Big Mac eaten in a light drizzle in Canterbury High Street, but now that a new lover had appeared, full of compliments about her beauty, she felt that this was her chance to practise her new chilly, aloof pose.

She demonstrated her unavailable look; which unfortunately looked remarkably like someone who'd taken one too many sleeping pills. Dorcas leaned over the toast rack with her eyes half shut and panted.

'Why are you panting?' I asked.

'I don't want to seem too hard to get. Foreign men are well known for the gifts they bestow on women,' she replied shortly.

It seemed most likely she'd get a free doner kebab and a portion of guacamole dip if she was lucky but I said nothing.

'Anyway, he's not Turkish,' she said. I couldn't imagine what culture shock he was enduring settling into a small market town and meeting Dorcas in all her glory. 'He's from Cyprus,' she added tersely, finishing her tea and getting up to go.

One of the things people mention when they are listing all the qualities of life in the countryside is that children have so much space in which to break the major limbs of their body. And so many varied opportunities to do so, ranging from falling off the scaffolding up the church tower [Harmony], falling off the ditch into the haha [Harmony] and falling off Tom's bike when he came round to give a lecture on the importance of wearing fluorescent clothing at night [Harmony].

As you may have gathered, Harmony, seen the length and breadth of Kent as a natural progression from the

Last of the Mohicans, spends all of her time outdoors haring around puce-faced at high speed on either two wheels, one wheel, or a pony with four legs. [Correction: it has four legs at the start of the ride but by the end it's probably lying on top of her in a festering ditch, its legs in the air and its eyeballs rolling around like a pinball machine.]

Harmony's great affinity with the equestrian world came as a shock to the family who thought it was just a passing phase that might last a few months. Three years later she still adores spending hours on a nag's back, preferably wandering around potato fields with a bunch of similarly minded young girls with dirty faces, dirtier jodhpurs and a predilection for lavatorial jokes at every opportunity.

When I was ten I can remember being mortified when my mother showed up at a school play and shouted 'BRAVO' loudly every time I walked on stage. Harmony is now at this stage of mortification, where the mere sight of me performing nifty steps to 'Tiger Beat' is enough to make her physically ill. She seemed to have hit that incandescent peak of hormonal hysteria about four years early, plunging from frenzied red-faced highs to periods of black gloom where she was forced to lie face down on her bed because no one loved her or understood her innermost feelings. 'What is the meaning of life?' she pondered, lying prone between Disco Barbie and a stuffed palomino. 'Where does life lead—to death and then what?'

For a hyperactive girl with a terminal tide mark and a pair of strong thighs, it led straight to the nearest pony school. This pent-up passion was not going to be channelled into poetry; her only attempt at school, aged three, had read 'Hat, Cat, Twat'—hardly poet laureate material.

And so Harmony began to ride. Every single week-end, and in ever-tightening jodhpurs, she would fling herself on to the back of an unsuspecting Bobbin, Popsy or Dibbin and race off round the fields hanging on to its neck. Occasionally she would agree to a proper lesson and be trained around the ring on a lunge rein, solemn-faced and stiff; meanwhile the pony breathed a sigh of relief not to have to perform cross-country feats hith-erto never attempted by a horse under seventeen hands.

The sartorial aspect of riding also appeals to Har-mony, which is odd as she has inherited much of her father's ability to put on quite new clothing and make it appear like the shrouds of someone long dead and exhumed last week. But for riding she suddenly longed with all her body and soul to be Elizabeth Taylor, wearing her hair in a net, a snood over her head, her legs encased in the tightest fawnest jodhpurs and the crispest cleanest shirts with cravats printed with either old-fashioned hunting scenes or raffish-looking foxes carry-ing half a pheasant in their mouths. And she saved up for a fox-head tie-pin and a gold bracelet with many dangling snaffles, stirrups and bits to complete her ensemble.

The riding bug had thoroughly attacked her last summer after a week away from home with her friend Rosie from school, staying with Rosie's granny Mrs Gollop or Mrs Dollop as she is affectionately known.

While staying there, Harmony and Rosie attended Lady Wispen's Riding Academy here in Compton Pauncefoot every day. It turned out to be the sort of place where wild-eyed red ponies raced around getting cream buns as prizes and playing musical bumps twice daily with a fourteen-course lunch for all the little girls in between, not forgetting a two-hour session of bum talk to keep everyone going. She came home determined to try her hand at gymkhanas.

But this summer Harmony seemed to have been rather jinxed. Every time a gymkhana was announced on posters stuck on to trees blowing in the wind, she was either unable to borrow a nag, or had one of those prior pressing engagements that crowd the social calendar of a ten-year-old. But I was frenziedly keen to encourage her love of the horse, feeling it was one way of staving off any possible interest in the love of the boy. Around here the demon under-ten disco scene is thriving with dozens of under-twelves regularly donning sequinned boob tubes and thigh boots and making off in the twilight to dance around their satchels in the scouts' hut at the end of our drive.

Autumn was now with us, and when the very last gymkhana of the season was announced on wispy bits of pink fly poster outside the post office, we knew this was the perfect opportunity for Harmony's debut. She'd borrowed a sweet-looking piebald pony with incredibly long eyelashes and a startling resemblance to Ian McShane. I just hoped it would be able to jump the necessary two feet in the air for beginners, although if it jumped like Ian McShane I wasn't holding out much hope.

It was good to have something extra to look forward to, as autumn in Kent, although beautiful in some respects, brings with it that sharp nip in the air that promises the endless long dark months of winter. Again, it is a case of being optimistic, looking at the glorious colours of the falling leaves, and welcoming all the local conker champions into the garden to assault our conker tree. Normally this consists of futile efforts to shake conkers out, followed by the throwing of schoolbags and stones up into the leaves to make them fall on to the ground. One evening I walked down the path towards the duck pond only to find a bespectacled little fellow throwing a broom up into the tree with a devilish expression on his face and very bulging pockets.

Our wisteria had long since dropped away, and been horribly brutally cut back by Lowther but was now replaced by the equal glories of Virginia creeper in a million shades of red, gold and orange. There also seemed to be more berries everywhere than usual; huge blue blackberries crowded all over the brambles near Lowther's cottage. Next to his front door, on our pride and joy, the massive ancient fig tree, a few solitary ripe figs still showed their heads through the vast leaves. Whenever I pass the fig tree I think of a neighbour of Sue's who is currently having therapy because of a terror of large leaves. Apparently he lies in fear of ever coming across rhubarb, and almost had to be hospitalised after someone inadvertently left a voluptuous cabbage on the back door step for his wife.

If you weren't looking on the bright side of the bounty of autumn, trying hard to think how wonderful it is that there are so many nuts around for the squirrels, you could depress yourself utterly, thinking about the horrible half-dead hanging baskets over everyone's front doors, and the browning flowers in the borders, and how in a couple of weeks there would be almost nothing presentable to stick in a vase, and it would be the usual five months of non-stop mock orange blossom instead. It still never ceases to amaze me that we can have so much space and no flowers half the year.

Harmony was very excited. She had the pony in training as though he was about to jump a puissance against David Broome. Short of carrying him over their practice jumps there was nothing more she could have done. The great day dawned, and Harmony was up at least five hours before everyone else, picking at his feet with a mediaeval torture instrument, shampooing his hair with my best shampoo and conditioner and sending Honey into apoplexy before breakfast by plaiting her best ribbon in his mane. Had the nag been entering the Miss Teynham beauty contest he would undoubtedly have won but it still remained to be seen whether he could actually lift both front legs upwards simultaneously.

Anyone who has attended them will tell you that Pony Club official events are very well organised, very competitive and filled with fat little girls pressed into salmon jodhpurs, as well as their braying mothers who have two Volvos and wear long-line Barbours with fur trims. Pony Club events are the thing we all dream of when we imagine our little girls riding for a hobby, neatly lining up on dapper little ponies, accepting a selection of rosettes before shouting, 'What ho, top hole' and riding around the ring. But it's also true that they are pervaded by a terrible feeling of pressure, as the mothers—who also rode in their youth—wring their hands together and take surreptitious swigs of gin out of hip flasks. Sometimes they even have to go and sit on the back flap of the Range Rover to cry when Sabrina and Vanessa fail dismally in the Bending Poles.

Pony Club devotees always staunchly claim that there is no class problem in the Pony Club. This is absolutely true as long as you have lots of money, a decent pony and four pairs of co-ordinating jods and hanky sets. It also helps if you go to a boarding school near Woking. A friend of mine took her daughter Ronnie and was virtually ostracised when: [a] it transpired that Ronnie went to the local state school and kept a hamster in her bedroom; and [b] her father became paralytically drunk in the beer tent and pinched all the mothers' bottoms.

This was not a true Pony Club event, which meant that some children were even wearing sweatshirts and there were a number of 'games' as well as the usual jumping and bending capers. It was also not as strictly or formally competitive as other Pony Club events would have been. I noticed that children who seemed to have tried very hard were given rosettes regardless of their final position. Twixes seemed to be part of the prize-giving ceremony too.

Harmony could hardly bear the suspense as she had to sit down through several other age groups before her turn to shine finally came. She was slightly disgruntled because she'd acquired a rather unpleasant stain down one leg, and Honey had managed to spill her pina colada on to her hacking jacket. These were mere trifles in the world of competitive sports, I told her—at least no one had attempted to psyche her out, or shoot the horse with a poisoned pellet.

'Golly, Mum,' she said sullenly at my attempts at levity, displaying her ability to make *Mum* into a fifteen-syllable swear word only heard on X-rated cable channels in dodgy motels near The Hague.

Then she was on. Harmony leaped on to the horse's back like the Lone Ranger and darted into the ring as though shot from a cannon. As the horse sped around the course, it was obvious from his desperately keen face that he realised that the only way he could be spared from becoming a burger in the next two days was to acquit himself well over the fences. Harmony's left buttock for some reason kept sliding sideways so that on two jumps she was at right angles to the pony but still grinning wildly.

Having always despised stage mothers I have to admit that I jumped to my feet, totally forgetting Harmony's ban on my humiliating her by 'being enthusiastic'. I shouted until I had to collapse in a heaving mass on the tartan car rug and replenish myself with half a Swiss roll and the rest of the Tizer. She had won, and we were thrilled. We couldn't have been happier *had* she won the puissance against David Broome; I was so proud I was convinced he'd be calling her later to get a few tips.

As she rode solemnly into the ring to collect her rosette and a two-day supply of horse nuts, the family rose collectively to its feet and shamed her by being too enthusiastic. Heavenly, in particular, loudly sang the Wedding March throughout all the presentations before walking around holding up the back of Honey's skirt like a small bald bridesmaid.

The rest of the day passed pleasantly as the pressure was now off. We could loll around admiring Harmony's rosette and drinking dandelion and burdock out of the bottle. All the girls from Lady Wispen's entered the Greedy Pony Contest, where the nags race up to the other end of the field where someone is holding out a handful of horse nuts and then race back having eaten them in one stomach-knotting mouthful.

Harmony did appallingly in the apple bobbing. She fell off the front of her horse into the trough of water where the red apples bopped and bobbed, soaking her svelte cravat. She and Honey also attempted the sack race, hopping along in sacks as they led ponies around as fast as they could. Harmony, unable to admit that she wasn't very good at it, blamed a boy on holiday from Weston-super-Mare for putting her pony off by farting audibly inside his sack.

It was so lovely that at six o'clock when it started to grow dark and chilly no one wanted to go home. We finally persuaded Champion the Wonder Horse into his box, and drove home through the sleepy winding roads, where Harmony fell into bed fully dressed, clutching her rosette to her heart.

A few days later I saw Dorcas at the Honeypot, grumpily eating a piece of fruit cake. She had held her Turkish waiter at arm's length with the sultry expression for a record three-and-a-half days, but had finally succumbed to his charms after he handed her a long box. She was convinced it was going to contain a glittering bracelet; in fact, it held an ornamental bottle opener from the Cinque Ports. She'd gone back to his flat over the off-licence next door only to discover he had decorated it in the Eastern mode. A tooled leather stereo unit was built into the headboard of the bed. He also had chasing red and green lights dancing up a disco inferno in time to his Duran Duran record. Around the room glass coffee tables rested on the great tusks of former wildebeest and the whole room was finished off by a wolfskin duvet and lemon yellow nylon sheets which glittered with static as Dorcas dumped her pale pink body on to the bed.

Despite being Compton Pauncefoot's answer to the Sheikh, it transpired that he was really a sheep in a wolf's duvet. He was horrified to discover midway through their passionate encounter that there was a two-millimetre gap in the leopard-skin curtains overlooking the High Street, and promptly rolled on to the floor and crawled on all fours up the corridor to the loo where he wrapped his groin in a J-cloth, which was all that was handy.

'How bourgeois,' she muttered darkly to me over her tea. 'Gawd, I really hate men sometimes. They're so wet. I want a man who's in touch with the animal in him.'

I said it hadn't looked as if Loveday from the hop farm had exactly been the missing link but she was unconvinced.

'I've decided I've got to see him again, so I'm going to have a fancy dress party soon to celebrate the ploughing contest—anything for a good excuse to get him round to my place.'

I agreed, and ordered a four-tier stack of cream cakes, two slices of banana bread and another pot of Earl Grey. You have to fortify yourself in the autumn, like the squirrels gathering their nuts.

CHAPTER 12

The Ploughing Contest
And The Ploughing Party

I<small>T WAS TIME TO PUT OUR CLOCKS BACK</small>. The days steadily grew darker and colder, although we were relieved to see that the weather seemed quite mild. This delayed the onset of the annual cold which our family passes from one member to another throughout the winter, constantly blaming the last person.

Lowther was busy trimming the hedges around the paddock. I watched him through the window as he cut the saplings through to a delicate halfway mark with one hand and then firmly twisted them through the stakes he'd battered into place, so that they would continue to grow and entwine until spring when they would once more burst into blossom.

We made daily pilgrimages into the woods at the far

end of the paddock and sometimes we went even further afield to the copse behind Millicent's house, stopping for tea and the inevitable plates of toast, buns and biscuits that are provided around here even if you pop in to borrow a stamp. Although the leaves had mostly turned brown and orange, the forests seemed alive with activity, with occasional clumps of green ferns, and various fungi growing out of technicolour mosses beneath the trees.

Unfortunately for us, the visibility of all of this fungi also coincided with the start of a lengthy television series about the delights of wandering the woods collecting wild fungi and then cooking them at home. Husband bought a small and ancient handbook and began peering under dock leaves, coming home with bowls full of quite obviously lethal mushrooms he wanted to eat.

'Ah,' we heard him muttering at a bright red spotted shaggy cap that could kill at twenty paces with or without the cream sauce. 'Hmmm, this could be a cept, don't you think?'

Lowther took it upon himself to have a look through the findings. He weeded out any that are usually used in Victorian murder stories and left me to cook the rest.

'Really, I don't know why you still go to the super-market,' Husband then informed me, avidly consuming a rubbery flat fungus he dug off the side of the summerhouse door. 'We could be self-sufficient here if you weren't so suburban about what everyone eats. A bit of mould never hurt anyone when I was a child.'

Only someone living in the town could imagine that

autumn was a time for winding down. On every walk we saw that the lanes were surrounded with fields full of farmers and their workers, still battling with ricks of corn and feeding the threshing machine. As the second rick they were building grew ever larger, it seemed such a wearying dusty job with very little thanks at the end of it. But I thought it must be excellent for the pectorals, as I noticed they all looked as if they'd be able to get new careers as Chippendales if they ever gave up farming.

The children loved to stop by the duck pond, which at this time of year was the place where the most comings and goings were occurring. It transformed itself into Grand Central Station, with ducks and geese waving little hankies at each other and flying off sensibly to Bournemouth and Bognor Regis. A huge flock of silly-looking coots arrived and they'd become charmingly tame because of the tender ministrations of local children—they would actually stand up and beg for bread. The swans and their two grey babies spent a great deal of time ruining all of this public relations activity by hissing and threatening everyone. The last time I ventured down, the father sat down on my basket refusing to budge, and as he was so big, flappy and fierce I left him sitting there until we returned from the market.

Walking up the hill home, the cow parsley was still in bloom here and there, but the children were most interested in the seeds. Nibbling on a sunflower seed, biting it in half, floods young mouths with the taste of sunshine and earthy autumn browns.

After one brisk autumn walk, we stopped at Brian's for tea, and discovered that he had a new scheme. He had just been out to place an advert in the window of the post office. It was emblazoned with the interesting phrase: 'Are you a glamour girl? Call me.' Brian said he was fed up doing weddings, and now the farmer had switched his banger off for the winter he felt it was safe enough to try some glamour photography.

'I'm going to do it in the garage. I've got a big red backdrop there—and an oil heater so the girls don't go blue.'

I said that I always imagined glamour pictures to be of girls frolicking on the beach with forty-inch bosoms.

'Well,' he pointed out. 'None of the beaches round here got the blue flag for cleanliness this year, so if I made them do that they'd probably go down with some dreadful runny ear thing.'

'Growler got diarrhoea when he went in the sea,' chimed in Honey.

'Growler gets diarrhoea going on the bus up the High Street,' I added.

'What's diarrhoea?,' said Heavenly.

It was time to go home.

As we walked in the phone was ringing. It was Reg Sourbutt from the Pick Your Own farm. Earlier that morning, when he'd had a bit of a setback, he said he'd remembered me visiting the farm back in the summer in all my splendour, wearing my track suit bottoms with Heavenly lying puce-faced and snoring on top of me under his hedge.

'You're famous-ish, aren't you?' he asked, which is one

of those questions no one English can answer, because we immediately have to act horribly coy and say, 'No, no,' despite the fact you might have been on fourteen magazine covers the week before.

'Well, that Day-Lewis feller had said he'd present my cup to the prize bullock at the ploughing contest on Saturday, but he just rang up and said he's got groin strain running.'

'And you want me to come to the ploughing contest and present the cups...' I answered. It's always best around here to know exactly what is expected otherwise you find yourself doing a jam-making demonstration in a side tent as well.

'Yup.'

I said that I'd love to, seeing I appeared to be the only celebrity available locally. 'Have you tried Dot Babcock?' I asked suddenly.

'Not Dot again,' he replied shortly. 'No one liked the way she kept shaking her leg all the time during the opening of your fete.'

So it was arranged that I would be there on Saturday, togged up in some town clothes so that I wasn't too much of a disappointment to everyone who came to see the presentation. I feared that most wouldn't feel they'd got their money's worth as after living down here for ten years everyone is totally used to the sight of me in my mouldering jeans, trying to drag my kids away from their mission to shoplift the Woolworth's Pick and Mix counter like some grimy latterday Fagin, and would not be able to suddenly case me in the light of a glittering starlet in the local firmament.

'Good, I'll tell my mother now,' he told me. 'She kept saying he seemed like a big London girl's blouse to her but when he let us down we felt very disappointed.'

As soon as I told her about the ploughing competition, Dorcas decided that it was the perfect excuse to lure the boy from the hop farm round to her place. She'd have a fancy dress party that night and invite him.

'No! Obviously not just him! Lots of people, so he won't notice when I corner him and see whether he wants to marry me.'

We then tried to work out what I should wear to present the cups to the horses and the prize bull.

'Just don't wear anything tight,' advised Dorcas. 'You'll only fall over.'

When I was at school we used to have weekly lessons on etiquette. I remember them well because they covered important topics such as where to sit the Pope if he comes to dinner at your home on the same night as the Queen Mother, and correct ways to address a letter of condolence to a sheikh or a deposed president. For some reason we also learned the language of fans and the polka, neither of which have been as much use as a couple of classes on how to use a poultry thermometer would have been, but that's the public school system for you. In no class, however, did we ever get tips on the correct apparel to wear for cup-givings. Having decided against anything black, tight or sequinned, we finally descended on a large poppy-strewn dress with a full skirt, which Dorcas said 'hid my multitude of sins'.

On the drive to the Pick Your Own farm, which the various contestants would helpfully plough up ready for next season, Dorcas and I sadly looked out of the windows of the car and wondered how long it would be before the whole of Kent was ruined in the way Ashford has been. The endless protests of Kentish people against the devastation of the Channel Tunnel has, of course, gone unheard; also in the name of 'progress', modern farming has to a large extent, even in this peaceful vale, wrecked most hedgerows.

But we probably won't miss them until they have all vanished and then it will become apparent that they were not just things of beauty with their tangle of hips, haws, hawthorn blossom and wild garlic plants which attract small clouds of butterflies. They are also sources of food for small animals, shelter and a place where rural remedies grow in their wildest state. If we are not made aware of their value soon, our hedges will all have disappeared, leaving vast spartan spaces of endless fields of yellow rape and little else between.

I have to say that even for Dorcas and I the ploughing contest was deeply boring, although it was very pretty. It was one of the few moments of rural life I found hard to wax lyrical about. Ploughing—like boules and train spotting, war games and yoga—is one of those things that you have to be a devotee of to spend an entire day watching. It's very hard to get truly worked up over who's going to take less than forty-five minutes to get to the end of the field.

All the breweries in the area had sent along their hugely powerful white dray horses. They ploughed away clad in a multitude of brasses, flags and small photos of the Royal Family, with their tails and manes done up in a mass of red ribbons which fluttered gaily in the strong breeze.

Another field, next to the home of the leaping pig, was devoted to a small market of local crafts. Stalls groaned with sweetly scented beeswax candles, unusual local apple juices and the usual hand-knitted lime green and pink stripy jumpers. In addition a large group of morris dancers from the local TSB flung themselves around a makeshift maypole with portly bodies, short legs and bright cherry red faces.

And then there was me. It had become apparent early on in the proceedings that really a celebrity should have been rooted out from considerably further afield, as no one local was fooled by my temporary celebrity disguise, despite my high heels and the large hat which kept getting blown drunkenly over one side. The high heels were very ill advised in the ploughed-up field; I had only worn them because I couldn't help thinking it would be humiliating to be shorter than the heifer you were awarding a prize to. Having said this I kept sinking up to my ankle in moist muddy soil before pulling my foot free again and soldiering on up the field with Dorcas chortling in my wake.

In the end it was all right I suppose, except for a slight wave of whispers which spread through the crowd as I approached the prize-winning bull, a massively muscled beast with a ring through its nose and an unpleasant sneer on its lips. It was unfortunate that I not only had to hand the large silver cup to the winning farmer who was beaming with pride and accompanied by his entire family, but also pin a rosette on to the beast's harness while he eyed me beadily, obviously longing to toss me and my stupid high heels fourteen feet over the nearest hedge. I was also wearing a dress with a very white skirt which kept catching on bits of thistle.

As I spun around to get the next cup off the table I realised what the wave of whispers had been about. It was nothing to do with me but Sue, who had just arrived to watch me perform my civic duties wearing an organza cowgirl's outfit with boots, spurs and a string tie. Her appearance was enough to stop anyone paying attention to the bullocks. As she tottered over to me through the rough grass she gasped excitedly.

'I'm so thrilled. They're going to open an isolation tank centre in Pratts Bottom next month, and I'm definitely going to be there suspended in silence for an hour. I just feel I have to rid myself of many earthly ties. We are all too materialistic and obsessed with possession. If we free ourselves of these demons I feel we can return to a more natural state.' She paused to buy four jars of honey and a toffee wafer, and slowly unwrapping it continued, 'Anyway I love Pratts Bottom. There's loads to do there. The weekend I go and get rebirthed again, I think I'm going to make you join me...'

After the ploughing contest, not only was everyone excited with the results but *tout* Compton Pauncefoot was at home struggling into their fancy dress costumes, happily unaware that the whole party was a ruse, one of Dorcas's many feminine wiles at work.

The more unhappy Dorcas had become, pining over her sleepy hop-picking Lothario, the more hops she had strewn around the house. Someone had bought her an off-the-shoulder red blouse back from a weekend trip up the Rhine, and so she had decided that she was going to wear that with a pair of fishnet tights and a top hat, and say she was a circus ringmaster. In order to wear the fishnets she seemed to have spent the past three days alternating between lying around with her Slendertone pads pulsating gently, or tripping down the hill to use Millicent's electronic runner-towel.

Loveday arrived just as the party was getting into full swing, and followed me, Sue and Dorcas into the kitchen where we were furiously replenishing our drinks and stabbing at green cocktail onions because Dorcas said they were sophisticated and gave a party glamour.

He didn't look at me, but stared miserably and intently at Dorcas's tin of strawberry Slimfast.

'I don't think it's going to work, Dork', he said. [I felt this was an unfortunate diminutive to employ.]

Dorcas picked up the electric whisk she uses on her pancakes and stared at him. She obviously wanted to whisk him to death.

'I don't think it's going to work,' he repeated.

'Yes it does,' she barked, thinking he meant the whisk.

'I had a triple stack with maple syrup this morning because it was windy outside.'

'No, you and me, Dorcas. It was fun that night, but I need to get my head together and I need space.'

I stared at him. He obviously thought he was Kent's Timothy Leary from the way he was going on to Dorcas. Anyway he'd slept through most of their date.

'But I'll always admire you,' he added.

Dorcas revved her whisk at him a couple of times, menacingly. Sue and I stared discreetly out of the window at the garden. Then a man from the fete committee walked in wearing a Roman toga, holding a ski and a long pole.

'Hey,' said Loveday completely forgetting the dramatic scene unfolding. 'That's a great outfit, who are you?'

'I'm Roman Pol-an-ski.'

'That's brilliant, isn't it, you two, huh?' And off he went to get another beer.

Dorcas turned to me and Sue, still revving her engine.

'Gorrrrd,' she said. 'I think my TV aerial might be brighter than him. I should have whisked him and pretended it was one of those weird domestic accidents. I actually know someone in Ospringe who tried to kill himself by jumping off his bed with the phone cord around his neck. It would have been like him.'

'Why bother?' I said. 'Let's wash up some glasses.'

Dorcas switched on *Bolero* and I switched on the tap.

CHAPTER 13

Ruralising

SUE MOVED INTO THE GOTHIC SPLENDOURS of her home a few years ago, and was determined to make it perfect in every way. Her days, she decided, were to be devoted to turning it into the most gloriously cosy and perfect house in Kent, if not the whole world. The house was going to be filled from top to bottom with the most splendidly soft sofas, covered in mountains of mediaeval cushions. Tartan club fenders would jostle happily with beaded pouffes and roses would pour over every single thing that wasn't tartan, beaded, frayed, distressed or a conversation piece. The whole incredible atmosphere was to be made even more throbbingly evocative of times past by the constant refilling of huge vases of orchids, lilies and amaryllis, all of which had to vie for air space with the four hundred joss-sticks permanently burning from the attic to the cellar.

To some this might sound as inspiring as Sue's eclectic taste in clothes, but to me it was different because I had been her friend throughout her wilderness years—the years in which she had not got the right home. Imagine taking the most beautiful red tiger lily and stuffing it in a Sani-lav container and you have the vision of Sue, in her old home.

For Sue used to live in Middlesex, in Keith Moon's old house, which was entirely empty, entirely white and had a black leather upholstered conversation pit in the middle of the biggest sitting room in the world. When Sue arrived at the house the first thing she spotted as she peered into the murky depths of the grimy kidney-shaped outdoor swimming pool was a Rolls Royce at the bottom.

Any house with a leather conversation pit is never going to be overtly cosy in winter. In summer it was even worse. The cold black tiled floors were reminiscent of an abattoir rather than a boudoir and the leather seats reached such temperatures that sitting on them in a pair of shorts could result in third-degree burns and a scorched G-spot.

In addition, throughout the wintertime poor Sue's home was plagued with damp, moths and such serious roofing problems that the whole floor was for entire seasons littered with potties, bowls and jugs collecting the incessant drip-drip-drips from the skies.

So when she moved to her new home, vast and perhaps forbidding as it could have seemed to one less visionary than her, she devoted herself to transforming it. First, she assembled a vast army of unsavoury-looking builders who she was convinced had also worked on Queen Nefertiti's tomb before travelling through oceans of time to help her get rid of her deathwatch beetle. She also spent hours haggling over church railings, stalking local antique shops and school fairs like a vigilante.

Not that she is the only one. Houses throughout this country are filled with husbands who lovingly spend the weekend sanding down their beams, repointing their rendering or staining a school bench they've snapped up for a large amount of money in a little antique shop somewhere.

The desperation of urban buyers of rural retreats to transform these properties into their vision of bucolic splendour is frightening. Sprigged wallpapers from Laura Ashley are pasted up; beams are thrust in where there were none; walls are plastered unevenly; damp courses are torn out to create a nice bit of terracotta mildew here and there; and Aga fever is an obsession.

While locals are all ripping out their ranges and installing shiny white Zanussis, or tearing up their red quarry tiles for a nice slick of lino or covering their wooden floorboards with a sweep of fitted Wilton, newcomers are positively despairing of their neighbours. They spend half their nights furtively sneaking around, inspecting all the local skips in case anyone has dared to chuck out a Tudor bathmat.

When we moved into the Priory, our biggest problem was that the sheer size of the rooms made all our possessions suddenly appear positively Lilliputian. Huge rugs that we'd imagined would carpet Shea Stadium looked more like prayer mats shrunk on a very hot wash, bed linen gave up seven inches before the end of every bed, and the vast pine kitchen table we'd hauled down resembled a hostess trolley suspended in limbo.

While other newcomers were installing everything with a sprigged floral pattern that had ever been invented, we found ourselves with a different passion. Anything with a story. Consequently I was seriously upset for some months after I discovered that Sotheby's had sold Napoleon's willie for only £200. Who wouldn't have paid double for that, I asked everyone? I would have given vast sums, I claimed to all and sundry, to have Napoleon's willie nestling on our fireside double-sized pouffe, in between the bound volumes of *Horse and Hound* and the framed photo of Harmony eating a lolly next to the Cresta Run.

Having been cheated of this trinket, Husband then came home with a framed piece of bread from the Siege of the Bastille and a boxed leaf from the tree under which Livingstone was buried which the Vicar's cleaner then vacuumed up, resulting in a total dismemberment of the industrial-sized Hoover. To add to the collection we also have Winston Churchill's cigar with a letter of authenticity from Lady Churchill.

I also noticed that Ralph and Debbie seemed to have succumbed to a terminal attack of ruralising. Their sitting room was filled with: small works of naïve art; sprigged curtains; rag rugs; pine bric-à-brac shelves;

huge pots of dusty dried flowers; a set of three views of
the Medway made entirely out of pressed pansies; and
a large eighteenth-century hoe which was propped
nonchalantly against the wall, next to Ralph's CD
player and complete collection of Russ Conway records
which he had cleverly hidden behind a ruffled gingham
curtain.

I was now permanently on the lookout for something
owned by someone historical. It was only a matter of
time, I thought, before I bought the bodice ripped off
by the hero of *Love's Throbbing Passion*.

There was no stopping us. A letter arrived from a lady
in Woking saying she had heard I was a keen collector
of Enid Blyton memorabilia—would I like to buy
Enid's old kidney-shaped dressing table with matching
stool, all in dusty rose chiffon? Husband contemplated
buying Boswell's wooden library chair and Words-
worth's chaise-longue while Sue tried to upstage us by
buying a surgical corset said to have been worn by Ted
Heath after he slipped on the poop deck of the *Gypsy
Moth*.

So conversations between Sue and myself altered
imperceptibly. We became true châtelaines, concerned
with how to get the best shine on our beeswaxed floors
[I drag two small children wrapped in a large fluffy
blanket over them], how to make bouquets of flowers
last longer [give them an Anadin and a spoonful of
sugar], and how to find loads of things for our houses
dead cheap [not figured that out yet].

A day out shopping with Sue veers frighteningly
between the spiritual and the dazing. One moment

you're trying to have an out of body experience, and the next she's herded you into a shop and is convincing you that a pair of Doc Marten boots with a gilt CC entwined on the front is well worth £300—they'll last all winter as long as you don't get them wet or dirty.

Today's plan was that we would go first to the car boot sale in the auctioneer's car park where she was hoping to buy a seven-foot tall stuffed grizzly bear with rampant arms and a hinged jaw. She was also on the lookout for a mock Gothic console table and a Murano glass mirror with matching bedside lamp. Out in the car park she was hoping to find a Raphael cartoon among some old prints being flogged for ten pence, or luck upon a Georgian diamond tiara with a broken hot water bottle thrown in for fourteen quid.

Lots of car boots were crammed with very pretty 1930s curtains and quilts and lots of slightly chipped picturesque china printed with cottages with rampaging borders and towering hollyhocks all painted in bright golden sunshine. I bought a box full of mixed pieces for a tenner and was well pleased.

Sue had turned into Arthur Negus and was clutching her *Miller's Antique Guide*. Snorting derisively at price tags, she would consult her book and then haggle the price down by at least forty or fifty pence every time. She ended up with two pairs of Chinese slippers [neither of them in her size and one with the shoes two different sizes], a pink ice tray with a large hole in it, and a lamp created out of a scale model of the Arc de Triomphe made of matchsticks. I pointed out that none of this looked unduly Gothic but she said it was all bargain stuff so she hadn't been able to resist.

As we went into the auction room, she immediately spotted a huge pair of red velvet tasselled swagged curtains. She had to have them, else she'd quite possibly die. Of course they were lot number 14,000, so we went out to a nearby Ye Olde Coffee Shoppe and fortified ourselves with crumpets and tea.

After several cups of steamingly fragrant china tea and a teetering mountain of hot buttery crumpets, drop scones and cream horns oozing with yellow cream, it was time to lumber back to the saleroom to bid for the curtains. Never having bid for anything before, she is one of those shy individuals who always leaves a discreet bid with the auctioneer but hardly ever gets anything because that's where the bidding always starts anyway. She couldn't decide what to do. Should she bat her eyelids at him in a meaningful way? Or wave her catalogue up and down in semaphore at him? Or perhaps grunt 'here' every time she was bidding? It was worrying and by the time she'd actually decided to simply wobble her catalogue, I'd bought two blue and white urns and a repossessed tumble dryer and she'd managed to acquire a stuffed auk in a glass cabinet filled with dusty dried grass. We were possessed with auction frenzy, which is similar to what my husband experiences when he sees other cars on the road and has to pound on their bonnets.

Auction frenzy means that even if you didn't actually want to buy something that much to begin with, the minute some other bastard bids, you suddenly find yourself willing to offer astronomical amounts for a pair of matching colanders.

Sue had happily stopped after half an hour of waving her catalogue so much that at one point I half expected aircraft to land on her mistaking her for an RAF batsman. She'd purchased the curtains, stuffed bear, stuffed auks, three runners, a pair of potties with a view of Rye on each one and a pair of mink earmuffs. She was now ready to go home to meditate, although she felt she might have trouble cleansing her mind of material possessions having just spent seven hundred quid in fifteen minutes.

We drove back quite tired as the tensions of bidding had taken their toll on both of us. Although I hadn't bid for that much, I noticed that my bottom imploded whenever Sue bid for anything, and that gave me hot flushes too.

'I dunno,' said Sue rather disconsolately when we got back to her house and were sitting in her beautiful vegetable-themed kitchen, with the Gothic pelmet on the curtains, each arch trimmed with a dangling silken radish or courgette. 'I dunno, I think I need to inspire myself with a shot of something more meaningful.'

I refilled her teacup as she drifted out of the room in her long swishing skirt; it looked as if she were on casters.

Sue called me from upstairs, where she wanted to show me something in her bedroom. The humidifier was on, spraying droplets of some noxious aromatherapy oil into the air. It made me feel like falling on to the bed with my legs in the air, except the whole of Sue's bed was always covered with major works of literature so instead I gingerly attempted to lower my bottom into a two-inch square space between Tolstoy and Solzhenitsyn. By the bed was her notebook where she writes everything down for her dream analyst in Woking.

'Look,' she said.

I looked up and Sue was in front of me, parading up and down in front of the window wearing a cardboard pyramid hat.

'I got it mail order from a company in Venice Beach that always advertises in the back of *Rolling Stone.* They sent me two free crystals and a civet spray with it.'

I said I hoped she wasn't going to wear it out to the WI. She looked at me as though I was the one wearing a purple cardboard pyramid hat.

'Of course I'm not. It makes my hair go really flat underneath.'

We opened the biscuit tin she keeps under her side of the bed and discussed pop stars we thought were gorgeous while she sat trying her hat out.

WINTER

CHAPTER 14

The Torchlit Procession

In Rio, Mardi Gras is celebrated in furnace-like heat; our own Kentish equivalent—The Torchlit Procession—is held as soon as it is truly cold, crisp and pitch black at night, on 5 November. It is not a Guy Fawkes event, but a rural celebration dating back hundreds of years. And, of course, no one in Compton Pauncefoot wears a thong.

Last year the epic undertaking coincided with the Centenary Celebrations which meant that the Vicar had terrible headaches of organisation. It's no wonder that he sometimes has to recycle the odd good sermon, and no wonder that he needs the odd night off at Shakers disco in Croydon.

'We did *The Canterbury Tales* and it was set around the market place last year,' he reminded me as we sat on the sofa in front of the vast log fire, our shoes off and our socks wiggling in the heat. 'It did confirm my feeling that no writer, living or dead, can be safe from being rewritten by the local clergy! Miss Gee, one of the wealthy local ladies, promised that she would generously donate to the funds if only she could be Elizabeth I in one of those terrible big white ruffs. No matter how much the Church Council reminded her that at no point does Good Queen Bess appear in Chaucer, she insisted we put her in.

'I'd written in this extra scene where the Queen rode through the market place, and as Miss Gee had never been on a horse before, I'd laid on this ancient mare. The Mayor was meant to point to Alderman Tyler and say, "Has the Queen come?" which I admit in retrospect was an unfortunate line. Sadly just as he uttered his line, a low-flying aircraft swooped down the whole length of the market and the bloody horse just took off with her hanging around its neck, her ruff asphyxiating her.

'We gave chase but the old horse made for open country clearing several hedges on its way. Miss Gee was found a couple of hours later by two elderly American tourists who couldn't get over how quaintly dressed we were in Kent!'

The Vicar had paid his call on me in order to discuss various themes of the procession. Local companies had been encouraged to hire lorries and create tableaux vivants for fund-raising and publicity; various members of the Rotary Club, daringly clad in costume, would collect money in buckets along the route. A number of smaller vehicles would carry along other local luminaries and societies. The Women's Knitting Circle were planning to sit in a circle knitting in the back of their Ford Transit. The May Queen, resplendent in peach polyester, would sit on a farmer's van with her attendants, with their deliciously red cheeks and crooked tiaras. They would be covered with a mosquito net to stop local yobbos throwing pennies at them. The polytechnic had a pantechnicon lined up with Millicent on it, and was doing a tableau based on a Hemingway short story—one of the poly's less assertive students was going to sit on all fours with two fake fur car seats draped over him and a pair of papier-mâché horns on a headband.

This sounded riotously entertaining, and if there were any problems with the lorries, the gaps were going to be ably filled by the various drum majorettes, Teynham Twirlers, pipe bands and acrobats who were also involved in this Vegas-like extravaganza.

But the Vicar turned to me wearily. 'There's been objections from the WI.'

'Why? It all sounds perfectly above board to me.'

'They're deeply worried about the tableau representing Nigel de Canterbury.'

Nigel de Canterbury, our local hairdresser, is a jolly attractive young man who has thrilled and delighted matrons for the past ten years with his various techniques with the blow-dryer. He is often seen in the local paper winning various hairdressing prizes for styles created entirely out of chopsticks and bright blue food colouring. I suspect this is his way of letting off steam after long days doing extremely straightforward shampoos and sets for the rest of us.

'What's he going to do?' I inquired.

'Apparently Nigel has asked an angry young man who is a friend of his to recite Oscar Wilde through a megaphone dressed in some kind of aesthetic costume holding a sunflower in one hand. And the lorry is going to be done up like the salon with one of those Hollywood-style mirrors with lights all around it. And Dorcas Plant is having her hair styled into a tribute to the church tower on St Perbold's.'

I didn't quite see the problem, but the Vicar explained that the young man who would be declaiming furiously from the back of the lorry was quite famous in the tabloids for having written a shocking bestseller about a rather disgruntled young man who falls in love with a sheep and is simultaneously angry about a wide range of social injustices. In addition, the Women's Institute ladies felt that he was obviously the type who would spoil everyone's day by reading only the 'unsavoury passages' from Wilde's many works.

'Have you asked Nigel to come up with some alternative suggestion?'

'Yes, but he was thoroughly spiteful, I have to say. He shouted at me, saying that if we tried to suppress his freedom of speech, he would have no choice but to use his secondary plan—a gaggle of girls from the Canterbury Secretarial College doing go-go dancing to a tape of "What's New Pussycat".'

I thought that sounded perfectly in keeping with the rest of the parade. The Vicar did have some good news to impart—the local Woolworth's had donated thirty pounds of assorted boiled sweets to be flung into the awaiting throng from the decorated vehicles. And with that cheering note we parted company.

I went down into town with the children and decided to treat them to a pre-Bonfire tea at the Honeypot, where we saw Brian, the photographer and honorary Mediterranean, buying a malt loaf.

He gloomily admitted that he hadn't had much success recently. Dorcas and a fourteen-year-old from the local comprehensive had been the only two replies to his advert for glamour girls. He'd been asked to do a poster for the Mango Marketing Board but had ended up having to spray a King Edward's potato pink and taking a snap of that because the mango wasn't the right shade.

I nodded, delighted to have proof that real food is *not* used in those cookery articles I'm constantly trying to repeat at home. As Brian was leaving, and the children were almost totally silent, buried in their Welsh rarebits, I heard Millicent calling to me, and invited her to join us. 'Looking forward to tonight?' she asked me.

'Yes—the fireworks, the baked potatoes, the toffee apples and then the procession—it's a lovely night,' we agreed.

'And then, of course, afterwards it's the run up to Christmas,' she laughed.

My very favourite time of the year is Christmas. As soon as 5 November is over, and the last dregs of mulled wine have been drunk by any friends taking part in the procession, I traditionally put my holly-and-ivy-covered tablecloth on to the kitchen table and begin to make mince pies and Yule logs. We are probably one of the few families truly sick of Christmas by mid-December as a result of my enthusiasm for the festive season.

By the time darkness fell, about forty local children had gathered in the paddock with their parents and were all waiting for Lowther to set alight the vast teetering bonfire. As soon as the flame touched the dry wood it flared up into the sky in a glorious splendid display and the smaller children merrily danced around it holding hands and singing at the tops of their voices, while their older brothers and sisters stood around, trying to look cool or waving sparklers around in the air spelling their names out in the iridescent light.

An hour later everyone was sitting on the damp grass with baked potatoes liberally stuffed with cheese, which none of the children would finish because they were longing for their toffee apples. The toffee was so soft that it stuck to their cheeks, hair and hands and was very satisfyingly hard to manage for the youngsters.

With half an ear I listened to Lowther making his annual firework safety talk to the assembled group before starting his display. I could hear him sensibly emphasising the importance of staying away from stray sparks, never looking at a firework and never ever throwing them. Unfortunately, at this point in the talk Lowther tripped over something lying in the grass [which I suspect belonged to one of my children] and fell on to the box of fireworks which tumbled over—but not before a stray spark from the bonfire accidentally ignited them. Lowther, the children, myself and Sue all had to lunge towards the trees like soldiers under a sudden bombardment.

A few minutes later the storm of billowing green, pink and purple sparks had subsided and Lowther emerged from behind a harshly pruned mock orange bush with a sheepish expression, obviously sad that he wouldn't be able to deliver his now-famous firework safety chat again for fear of this unfortunate incident being mentioned as an example of what can happen.

Honey was crying because she'd laddered her new tights and her ribbon had come out so that her Madame de Pompadour hairstyle was listing to one side. Apart from that no great injuries had been sustained unless one counted Lowther's pride which I fear had been further dented in the unseemly scuffle for the undergrowth.

All the fireworks were burned to a crisp. Harmony lit her sparkler and we all looked at that instead until it fizzled to a finish. At least we had the procession to look forward to next.

Lowther, Cedric, Ralph and Debbie, Karen and Laurence Young and Simon and Tom joined us on the walk down to the town itself. The procession was already snaking its way slowly around the town's narrow streets. The drivers of various overloaded articulated lorries and small vans were driving carefully as the crowds spilled on to the road here and there and small children dangerously darted out to pick up the boiled sweets that were flung from the floats.

Cedric and Brian were both on the tech's float, which had turned into a Roman-themed spectacle. Both of them wore sheets and were being flogged by the PE teacher from a local boys' college. Nigel de Canterbury's float was an enormous hit as it carried the dancing girls from the secretarial college. He'd had a fight with the operatic writer friend.

The town, Ralph mentioned happily, couldn't look more beautiful. He and Debbie had continued to join every possible society, institute and organisation, and he was now one of the leading lights of the Iron Society which was responsible for erecting ornamental bollards carrying the Swale coat of arms, as well as hanging baskets of lobelia on the library and town hall.

Certainly, as we stopped and watched from our little spot overlooking the pond and the procession, everything looked charming. Firelit torches hung from the lamp-posts and others were held by the doublet- and hose-clad members of the Cricket Club. It all looked very mediaeval, and the red laughing faces of the local mothers hanging from their upstairs windows calling to each other gave the night a painterly quality.

Our family and our friends thought for the millionth time how lucky we were to live here in such a beautiful place, and with the sleepy children held up on our shoulders we ambled home in the firelit night.

CHAPTER 15

Rebirthing In Pratts Bottom

IF YOU LOOK ON ANY MAP OF KENT, close to Sevenoaks but not far by car from the outskirts of our area you will see a small hamlet that has become a centre for all the New Age nouveau hippies of the county—Pratts Bottom, where a new wholefood holistic centre has now opened.

It is here that one would travel for Chinese herbs to cure childhood eczema, for homeopathic remedies for any ailment, and for aromatherapy oils, unguents and massages. Wearing your pyramid hat in the street would not cause a second glance from the inhabitants, who live in small cottages and wear tie-dye kaftans and earth boots with jumpers knitted from muesli.

Naturally, Sue is in her element here. She often comes to see her clairvoyant to check whether or not she should take the hovercraft to Calais, among other life-enhancing queries. As well as the masseurs, potters and vegans selling beans, pulses and lentils in the local shops, there is also the afore-mentioned centre where rebirthing classes are now held. And it was to rebirth that Sue and I found ourselves travelling the week after the bonfire.

As we drove over to Pratts Bottom, we sat in the companionable silence of old friends, admiring the wintry scene outside. November is a hard month in the country. Everyone must make a real adjustment to the cold and the dark, especially knowing that it stretches ahead for many long months. The weather had been most difficult over the past week. Clinging mists hovered low over the paddock every morning when I woke up, and the night before, when I returned home from Sue's, a terrific storm woke us all.

The sky was alight with slashes of lightning and bolts of thunder rocked the house and tumbled over the countryside. The noise went on for a couple of hours, leaving us sleepless but also making us feel cosy inside our snug beds. The ill-fitting stained glass windows all rattled worryingly and since the great storm some years ago, when we lost sixty per cent of our trees, we have been afraid that the old oak in the middle of the paddock might be hit and harmed.

Then, in the early hours of the morning, when the storm was finally spent, and after a large lump of the crumbling masonry of the tower had plummeted in to the sand pit below, a frost descended, white and freezing and enshrouding everything. This morning, as I drove past on my way to Sue's, I noticed that even after just a few cold hours part of the pond had frozen over, which would thrill small boys if it froze completely in the next weeks.

We made our way to Pratts Bottom as starlings and magpies swirled in the skies above us like little bits of soot. I thought how happy I would be to get a hot drink.

Sue was happy—partly because she'd finally put the great auk she bought at the auction up in the bathroom and it looked splendid, and also because she'd got this appointment despite the fact that the centre had been fully booked, but they had had a cancellation from a lady in Tenterden who had a bad case of cystitis following a seven-hour session of tantric sex.

Sue sang along to her Bob Dylan record, practised her deep breathing at traffic lights and started to ponder whether she might have been Edith Sitwell in a past life.

'I'm thinking of trying rolfing next,' said Sue when she'd finished gasping.

'Why?'

'Oh, mainly because I saw the man who does the rolfing, and he was totally gorgeous, like a cross between Harry Belafonte and Byron. I thought he could definitely massage the inside of my nostrils any time.' I meditatively ate a bag of pork scratchings, and we arrived safely.

Of course I shouldn't have let myself get excited at the prospect of a hot drink. Refreshment finally came in the form of one of those New Age hippie teas: camomile and cow's foot, which tasted mind-boggling.

A woman in pink dungarees with a large hankie tied around her head offered us both a slice of vegetarian banana bread. Sue whispered loudly out of the corner of her mouth that all the women were obviously lesbians and that she was feeling nervous. I calmed her down by insisting that anyone male, or female, would have to be almost superhumanly attracted to her in order to get past all her petticoats.

The largest room at the centre, next door to the rolfing waiting-room and the wholefood café, had many striped mattresses laid out on the floor in rows. In the middle I noticed a girl in a lilac tie-dyed cheesecloth smock trimmed with two bells carrying a small baby in a papoose. She came over and told us she was in charge of the session.

She looked Sue up and down, pausing to look closely at the small bunch of velveteen violets she had pinned on to her hairband.

'You'll have to take those petticoats off,' she said. Sue blanched, convinced that there was an ulterior motive for this request.

'I'll take the top eight off,' Sue compromised with dignity. I sighed. I hoped this wasn't going to take forever as I wanted to get home for the repeats of *All Creatures Great and Small.*

Our leaderene told me to stay at Sue's side throughout her rebirth. 'Sometimes rebirthing in Pratts Bottom can get out of hand,' she told us conspiratorially. 'Sessions in Islington often do, I've noticed, though people's emotions *are* very free in North London. You're all so repressed round here.'

Rebirthing involves a deep-breathing process too complicated to explain here but suffice to say it makes most women in labour look like they're having tea with the Queen Mother. Sue was hard at it gasping away, so I mopped her head with a horrible hot towel, and pulled one set of false eyelashes off which made her pause and glare at me. But as the room packed with clairvoyants, New Agers, hippies and a market gardener from Canterbury, all approaching the climax of their past life experiences, Sue, it seemed, was not there with them.

Half of her was returning to the primordial swamps of the womb, but another half of her wanted to go to the loo, and her need to pass water had totally overtaken any interest she had in reliving her experiences in the birth canal. She was mainly wondering where the 'person's toilet' was—this was the sort of institution that calls God She and talks constantly of people-hole covers.

It was no good. Sue couldn't concentrate every fibre of her being on the process as she was too worried about wetting her remaining fourteen petticoats. She trotted off to the loo in her Chanel pumps and I was handed yet another cup of comfrey tea, this time with a solitary cinnamon stick thrust in it.

As we left the building we bumped into someone coming in. He was exceedingly thin, wore an Angela Davis tee-shirt and had long hair like a sexy floor mop. He gave a Black Panther salute to Sue and knocked her hairband off. 'Have you feasted with Mammon?' he asked.

We gazed back at him, and he stared at Sue unblinkingly like a yellow-eyed reptile. Then he pushed past us and went into the centre.

'That's him,' said Sue gesticulating wildly in the general direction, 'the one I want to rolf me.'

While Sue and I drove home she said that while the experience had lasted it reminded her very much of a dentist's drug. 'The whole thing reminded me of that time I had to take Perce to have his wisdom teeth out. He staggered out at the end, threw two felt tip pens at a couple of old ladies in the waiting room and shouted at the Mayor who was there for a root canal, yelling, "Are you out there, London," as though he'd just completed one of his twenty-minute drum solos at Wembley.'

'Gosh,' I said, swerving to avoid a fox that darted right across our path. We swerved into her driveway, only to spot lights and a small bonfire ahead of us.

'Oh my God,' said Sue, stricken. 'They look like those travellers you see trying to haul themselves over the fence at Stonehenge on Druid days. What on earth are they doing in my woods?'

'Peace,' said one of them, stepping up to the car which had ground to a halt.

'We heard that you were a fellow sister, and we knew you wouldn't object to us pitching our humble yert here for the night. You're welcome to join us,' he said.

Sue was grey, and grappling in her bag for a Veganin.

'No,' she replied weakly.

'Hey baby, what sign are you?' he added, grinning to reveal no front teeth at all. But Sue was busy Sellotaping her tablet on to her head. It was time to go home.

CHAPTER 16

Christmas Holidays At Last

IN THE MIDST OF ALL THE COLD BLEAKNESS comes the jewel of the year, the glittering ruby-red festive season which ends the year so perfectly. Despite the fact that all around us friends and neighbours were dropping from a particularly virulent form of flu, the thought of Christmas and all its treats was enough to keep me going throughout the main part of December. I didn't succumb to the colds or the flu, as it would not be possible for me to lie down for more than fifteen minutes at a time. I had shopping, wrapping and present-buying feats to perform.

Honey came home thrilled with herself. She had been chosen to appear in her school play as an angel, a role she was delighted to play, as it involved wearing a long white gown with huge glittering silver paper wings tied on to her back with tinsel. A tinsel halo would be held

216

aloft by an unbent coat hanger stuck firmly on her headband.

It had been a difficult month for Honey. She had been very worried that she might have to play one of the cattle or, worse still, a sheep in the nativity scene. This would have meant the indignity of staying on all fours and lowing occasionally and also being covered in one of the Vicar's car rugs. One of the great attractions of the school play for Honey was the singing, and she was hoping there would be long pauses in the narrative where she could burst into a loud selection from *Oklahoma* which she particularly likes.

There was also the strong possibility that as soon as the innkeeper exited stage left, she might lean soulfully on the manger, say, 'Thank you. And now I'd like to do a song that's been very kind to me,' to the assembled parents and launch into a smouldering torch song of the type normally sung by Hollywood sirens of un-certain age on their comeback tours.

Honey's main worry was for animals. This year she became a vegetarian, after going into a butcher's shop where whole carcasses swung from the ceiling for the first time. This made her put two and two together and no meat has passed her lips since. Nor those of anyone else in the family, as the tears and recriminations each time a sausage appeared were almost too much to bear. Since then it has been soya quorn and Linda McCartney burgers, and while we eat a small but insistent voice now interrogates us on the future health of thousands of Christmas turkeys.

This change in our diet meant that my husband

became almost crazed in his search for meat. Dracula could not have yearned for a steak tartare more. He began to secretly consume bacon sandwiches in the dead of night, and as soon as he went out to lunch he would desperately suggest Angus Steak Houses all over the county. He was like an alcoholic with a terrible secret craving. I half expected piles of offal to pour out of the bottom of our wardrobe, along with the ten-year-old copies of *Razzle*, each time I opened the doors.

There was another grey culinary cloud on his Christmas horizon. I was again attempting to give up sugar, since I'd developed a large hole in my front tooth in the summer holidays. Christmas was beginning to look doomed.

I found my husband peering gloomily out of the window. Was Christmas to be a barren wasteland consisting of two nut cutlets and a sugar-free jelly? Wasn't the true meaning of Christmas largely in its celebratory fare, i.e. a huge turkey big enough for small children to ride around the garden on, and massive helpings of Christmas pud, with lashings of cream, flames leaping off it and holly alight on top? And what about later on? Was he going to be sitting in his armchair surrounded by family and friends eating a bowl of kelp-flavoured crisps and a few additive-free diabetic boiled sweets, instead of the usual tin of Quality Street, four boxes of After Eight mints, the ten-pound bag of nuts and the jug of mulled wine melting the veneer casing on the telly?

Depression descended as he remembered Christmasses past when there was no embargo on meat, sweets and all things good to eat in our home. With dread, he looked forward to Christmasses in the future where, no doubt, Honey would become more and more militant, changing from Baby Doll into Hanoi Jane before our eyes. Instead of worrying about her being out at an all-night party, we'd be tossing and turning about whether she'd turn out to be one of those people wearing a balaclava back to front as they make night-time raids on abattoirs. And no sweets, a dearth of fattening foods wrapped entirely in foil dotted around the house in small silver bowls ... It didn't seem like Christmas.

A compromise of sorts was obviously needed, but it would be hard when dealing with such a rabidly proselytising vegetarian as Honey.

Lowther had now cut everything in the garden back to a crewcut stubble, which made it look as if he'd actually used Agent Orange to get rid of the bind weed, but the garden was still bravely showing signs of life, I noticed early one morning when I went out to pick armfuls of holly and ivy for my decorating.

The ivy always flowers in late December. The little flowers shaped like balls are filled with a deliciously strong nectar that seems to half-drug moths and other insects so that they almost fall out of the pale green blooms like drunks at closing time. Although I am always moaning that we do not have enough cutting flowers, at this time of year there is no shortage of decorative plants and branches. Huge red shiny rosehips cover the cloister garden where climbing roses once tumbled, holly berries stand out against the dark glossy green leaves with their frighteningly sharp edges and soft white snowberries perched on bare twiglets are ready to be brought indoors and entwined around the staircases, the window sills and the mantelshelves.

One evening we all stood outside to watch a vast blood red sunset—only a few more days and it would be Christmas. Lowther walked over to join us, admiring the spectacle.

'Red skies at night,' he said congenially. 'That means we're going to have a nice spell of mild weather, so country lore has it.'

The next morning we woke up to find the whole valley hidden beneath the thickest snow for ten years. We all fell out of the front door wrapped up in layers of clothing and huge thermal gloves. We saw Lowther on his way to the shops to stock up on milk and other essentials; he waved rather sheepishly to me. But it didn't matter. The snow covered everything, hiding every imperfection under its thick pristine whiteness. The fox and his mate had been down to the duck pond earlier and had left their tiny tracks across the lawn. Honey let her rabbit down in the snow, but unable to find any grass Ferdipan soon wanted to get back into his handbag for shelter.

The numerous spiders' webs hanging off the doors and porches around the house were picked out in a delicate filigree of frost. Everywhere looked like a perfect Christmas card. I only hoped none of the pipes would burst.

The children and their friends were well pleased with the change in the weather. While I decorated the house with mistletoe I'd gathered, and Lowther put a vast bowl of Christmas roses into position in the hall, they spent hours sliding down the hills near the vegetable garden on makeshift toboggans made of the huge strong plastic bags that Lowther's fertiliser came in.

I am always extremely careful with my foliage. I know now how it can become very desiccated, making perfect tinder when lit. When we spent our first Christmas in this house, we travelled hurriedly and unwisely from London on a chilly Christmas Eve and I left the turkey on the doorstep of the house in London. I failed to realise my error until we'd arrived in the depths of the country. I was hugely pregnant and I remember clearly that the cloister door had blown open and great drifts of dead leaves had piled up all along the hallways, not a sight conducive to great cosiness or festive cheer.

Having constructed what I felt was an imaginative display of red and gold candles nestling amongst various evergreen on the mantelpiece, I retired to the kitchen to baste the fish fingers [seven of them] which was all we had for lunch. Seconds later I returned to find the entire room thick with smoke, half the panelling smouldering and the mantelpiece burning as merrily as the fire in the grate. I am now very careful how I heat my pine cones.

I drew up a list of who was coming to the house. As usual the comings and goings formed a complicated pattern, not unlike one of those excitable dances on 'Come Dancing'. Although my preparations invariably begin after the Torchlit Procession, with the ceremonial unveiling of the holly-and-ivy table cloth, this year, as always, by the week before Christmas it became apparent that I was way behind couples like Karen and Laurence Young who did all their shopping for presents in the January sales, and wrapped them all last month when they restocked their freezer as well.

These people, of course, looked fresh and happy, whereas I was grey and a bit pinched, because the hideous spectre of an afternoon being elbowed in the liver by a lot of crazed Christmas-shopping mothers in Canterbury was looming on my ill-prepared horizon. Husband, who was almost catatonic from the stress of buying my present and wrapping it, as usual took up his position with one leg up on the club fender, and told me I shouldn't do so much. If I'd done my shopping in the January sales and wrapped them in a lull in the summer holidays I wouldn't be 'looking so wizened'.

The children and I spent a happy day detangling the fairy lights and erecting the tree, which was bigger than the one in Trafalgar Square, we decided. We hung balls on every branch in sight, so that it shimmered, sparkled and glittered in the firelight and then we covered it in a silvery stuff that danced in the light.

As I walked past their house I noticed that Debbie and Ralph had one of those plastic trees made out of the shredded stuff normally used to line the inside of

Russian cosmonauts' underpants, which meant that their tree could travel to Uranus with no problem. They had stuck three limp fronds of tinsel on to it and put their feet up until next year, although from the un-festive sounds of Gothic music coming from within, the comrades were staying the week.

Christmas approaching is always a time of agony and ecstasy. The exhausted panic that you feel having gone out and bought things you'll never need, only to discover that you've got no stuffing and the shop has shut firmly for the holiday. The thrill of knowing you've spent all the money you were likely to earn in the coming year on bizarre presents for absolutely anyone you've ever met.

Along with ignoble thoughts hoping that you don't get another green porcelain pomander for Christmas, there was the endless running-through of mental lists, ticking off things to be done, and wondering about the guest list—Sue and Perce, our annual Christmas guests Chris and Kathy, and all the other neighbours who would simply pop in for mince pies and mulled wine. I always find myself acting as though the tiny local shop at the top of the hill is going to be shut for three months rather than three days. Feverishly I stock up with bread and toilet rolls, so that if war ever breaks out during Christmas week our family will have enough toilet rolls for its duration.

On Christmas Eve it was all done, and if it wasn't done I was past caring about it. The local choir came around on their annual turn around the houses, this year slightly hampered by the thick snow. It was a delight to hear their voices soaring in the darkness outside, their faces lit by a lantern held aloft by either Ralph or Debbie, who had joined the choir some months ago. It made Christmas seem a real moment of rejoicing [it hadn't seemed so in Canterbury earlier where I saw two housewives coming to blows over a Yule log which was reduced in price because its robin appeared to have dropsy].

Honey joined me at the door, singing along with a few heartfelt choruses of 'I who have nothing' while the choir tackled 'God Rest Ye Merry Gentlemen' with gusto. When they had left, having gratefully drunk a gallon of mulled wine and polished off the first batch of mince pies, the children and I decided to walk down the hill to the town. They were very excited about Santa's imminent arrival and so a walk might calm them down.

The snow on the ground was a little slushy from shoppers making their last-minute preparations, but on the rooftops and gardens it was still hard and perfectly white, like soft fur. Compton Pauncefoot was as beautiful at Christmas as it was in the blazing heat of the summer, but with an added air of expectancy, excitement and delight.

Everywhere looked splendidly Christmassy, as it would in a nostalgic old film. It never ceases to amaze me how the shops in London all club together but end up with no more than a few miserable bits of very modern-looking plastic sheeting printed with snow-flakes, with no thought of the magic of the season. Every single year in Compton Pauncefoot, the streets are strung with multi-coloured lights, and alternate lamp-posts are decorated with a nude robin or a great big snowman with a very erect broom. In the late afternoon, when it is already properly dark, nothing could look more like a traditional Christmas scene as large white snowflakes plop out of the sky.

Shop windows are filled with decorations—at the butcher's, this year, a plaster sheep and four lambs sat around a crib; at the general store four pairs of pink knickers and a thermal vest were trimmed with some holly, one glittering sign which said 'Goodwill To All Men' and another which said 'Vests Half Price Upstairs'. The Honeypot was, as always, ablaze with lights, and displaying a crib surrounded with currant buns.

Back home, all the presents were neatly wrapped and hidden in the power shower, where no one would ever think of looking as everyone is so frightened of getting wet. I felt I had chosen appropriate gifts for everyone. Beloved had many pairs of socks, a subscription to the *Spectator*, and a telescope for gazing at the heavens during sleepless nights. Harmony had a plaster pony and trap, a new pair of jodhpurs with a very smart jacket to match, and a new whip. Honey had several Barbies [including one in a perfectly splendid princess outfit], a bag full of new Barbie shoes, as she'd eaten the last lot, and a pink sequinned tutu with a marabou feather trim. Heavenly had a baby doll with several little matinée jackets, a toy ironing board and plastic iron, and two brushes and dustpans as she is a small girl obviously sent to earth to send feminism back twenty years. I was hoping for a pair of shoes and no pomanders this year.

Chris and Kathy arrived. Chris is a loud, theatrical irresistible character who brings a Hogarthian flavour to the proceedings by singing falsetto Elizabethan madrigals and burping in time to 'Jingle Bells'. Kathy is a goddess in skintight black velvet.

The house hummed with a palpable feeling of great expectancy as finally Christmas Eve was upon us. The children lay sprawled out in front of the log fire writing their letters to Santa. I noticed that Harmony's started with an apology for shouting 'You don't own me, you bumwipe' last week when I mentioned innocently that I thought green teeth didn't go with her new leggings. Honey said that she was sorry that she'd run into Boots and put lipstick all over her face. Heavenly luckily cannot write, otherwise who knows what confessions Santa would have had to read before setting off.

Before they went to bed, they laid out a carrot, a mince pie and a glass of milk for Santa. Honey was already feeling agitated as it had begun to worry her that Mrs Claus would be making Santa a turkey dinner for when he returned home. 'Poor little turkeys,' she muttered, her eyes filling with tears. 'Not a very merry Christmas for them.' I hung their stockings over the end of their beds, and put a disposable nappy for Heavenly at the end of ours, as her presents always come in her nappy.

Finally silence reigned. The children were asleep, the mulled wine was stewing on the cooker, and we were awaiting the first of our guests who were to accompany us to the midnight mass service. Despite the company, I staggered up to bed, unable as usual even on this miraculous night to manage to stay up past nine o'clock. Even when I do I feel bad tempered and invariably fall asleep on the sofa with my mouth wide open.

Dorcas told me that the church had been, as always, full of slightly drunken devotees at Christmas midnight mass, but the Vicar was delighted to have a full house. He had given an expansive sermon on goodwill to all men in the coming year, which thrilled all the people in the front row. Usually on Sundays one can hear every individual voice readily singing against the plinkey-plonkety warping sounds of the rather damp village organ. The Vicar wobbles on his high notes and then plunges off the edge in worrying descants which no one else realises are in the hymns. Lowther hums along occasionally, bellowing out the odd word here and there, while Millicent always sings everything as though she's a nightclub singer in Beirut.

This year there had been so many people that there was standing room only next to the Vicar's famous samovar. Everyone had been packed so closely together that there had been no way of spotting which culprits were singing totally flat. Certain merry members of the congregation, drunk from the heady combination of the atmosphere and fourteen pints at Lord Spencer's Slug Pellet, had actually sung the words to the wrong hymn completely, and other elderly ladies of the parish had trilled an aria from *Iolanthe*.

Occasionally the scent of our mulled wine, which I had left fragrantly brewing, had wafted under the huge oak doors leading into the church itself. This caused an immediate rash of sniffing from Low Church members in case the Vicar was attempting to infiltrate the service with frankincense and myrrh.

The revellers woke me up again so I stumbled downstairs and bid a final good night and a loving Happy Christmas to the assembled merrymakers. Dorcas had arrived looking very chirpy. Sue and Perce were sitting at the kitchen table. Sue looked like the finale of *White Christmas*, wearing a beautiful red velvet floor-length gown trimmed with cumulus clouds of white swan's down. Even Millicent was there, rumbling ominously about the Vicar's Christmas sermon. 'I never knew he'd been at drama school with Gareth Hunt,' I overheard her saying. 'No wonder his voice always carries so well.'

Despite the endlessly creaking floorboards, the children's presents were duly delivered. It is a testing time though, with the fear that Sparkle-Eyes or Barbie might fall crashing to the floor, waking them all up. I dreaded the prospect of a tired and emotional Honey needing to put mascara on before being coaxed back to bed at three in the morning.

Then we all headed off to bed, Chris and Kathy eager for the safety of the electric over-blanket before being woken up the next morning by Harmony's small, over-excited and freezing cold body squeezed between them.

The next day we opened our presents by the fire. Having played with everything, we took a short walk around the frozen garden admiring the frosty branches before lunch.

I had tactfully hidden the turkey in a small closet leading off the dining room, so everyone had to secrete themselves in there to carve any meat they wanted, which added an interesting air of secrecy and adventure to the proceedings. 'Poor little turkey,' Honey intoned mournfully again, as she saw Chris's laden plate. 'Not much of a happy Christmas for him, is it?' But luckily, excited by her new presents, she refrained from staring in an anguished manner at each mouthful he ate.

Having watched the Queen's Speech lying sated on the floor [I was, not the Queen] I pulled out my large tin of Quality Street and gave it to Sue to pass round. Sugar was once more on our menu—I would have to wait till Resolution Time to give it up once more. I wondered what Millicent was going to be giving up again in the New Year.

The Vicar arrived wearing a new cape an admiring lady parishioner had made for him in the sewing circle. We all agreed he looked most dashing, and very svelte. It was obviously time for our annual torturous games of charades.

Millicent was given *Xanadu*, which I felt was almost impossible to perform. As she kept leaping up into the air, everyone annoyingly shouted *Horse of the Year Show* at her, which must have been very disconcerting. As befitted someone who had been at drama school, the Vicar turned out to be rather wonderful at charades. He even coped admirably with 'When the Swallows Come Back to Capistrano.'

But it was watching Sue, attempting as she does every year to mime Big Country, that brought home to me one of the great joys of country living. For all the changes we have seen around here in the past decade, for all the new friends we have made, some things always seem to remain comfortingly the same: the sense of happiness and well-being, the warmth of knowing your neighbours, the joys of the fireside, the creativity inherent to a life spent in the country. Perhaps it seemed all of that was captured by the annual sight of Sue in her many petticoats, a mince pie in one hand and a fan in the other, once again taking her turn in Christmas Charades and, for the tenth year running, manfully coping with *Swedish Blow-Job*, a charade she has made hers alone.